C00 529 935X

D0682122

The Famous Five's Survival Guide

Enjoy more childhood adventures with the Famous Five,
the original child adventurers!

Title	Publisher	First Edition Date
Five On A Treasure Island	*Hodder & Stoughton*	*September 1942*
Five Go Adventuring Again	*Hodder & Stoughton*	*July 1943*
Five Run Away Together	*Hodder & Stoughton*	*October 1944*
Five Go To Smuggler's Top	*Hodder & Stoughton*	*October 1945*
Five Go Off In A Caravan	*Hodder & Stoughton*	*November 1946*
Five On Kirrin Island Again	*Hodder & Stoughton*	*October 1947*
Five Go Off To Camp	*Hodder & Stoughton*	*October 1948*
Five Get Into Trouble	*Hodder & Stoughton*	*October 1949*
Five Fall Into Adventure	*Hodder & Stoughton*	*September 1950*
Five On A Hike Together	*Hodder & Stoughton*	*September 1951*
Five Have A Wonderful Time	*Hodder & Stoughton*	*September 1952*
Five Go Down To The Sea	*Hodder & Stoughton*	*September 1953*
Five Go To Mystery Moor	*Hodder & Stoughton*	*July 1954*
Five Have Plenty Of Fun	*Hodder & Stoughton*	*July 1955*
Five On A Secret Trail	*Hodder & Stoughton*	*July 1956*
Five Go To Billycock Hill	*Hodder & Stoughton*	*July 1957*
Five Get Into A Fix	*Hodder & Stoughton*	*July 1958*
Five On Finniston Farm	*Hodder & Stoughton*	*July 1960*
Five Go To Demon's Rocks	*Hodder & Stoughton*	*July 1961*
Five Have A Mystery To Solve	*Hodder & Stoughton*	*July 1962*
Five Are Together Again	*Hodder & Stoughton*	*July 1963*
Five Have A Puzzling Time, And Other Stories	*Red Fox*	*October 1995*

Enid Blyton™

The Famous Five's Survival Guide

WITH THE NEW

Unsolved Mystery

A division of Hachette Children's Books

First published in Great Britain in 2008 by
Hodder Children's Books

A catalogue record for this book is available from the British Library

ISBN: 978 0 340 970836

Printed and bound in China

Hodder Children's Books
A division of Hachette Children's Books
338 Euston Road
London NW1 3BH
An Hachette Livre UK Company
www.hachettelivre.co.uk

See Page 253 for individual copyright holder details.

Warning

When one undertakes to have adventures like the Famous Five, one runs the risk of coming across sticky, and sometimes dangerous, situations. If you plan to undertake adventures like those described in this book, we absolutely insist that you do so under the supervision of (and with the permission of!) a responsible adult. Please always follow their advice and guidance – in adventurous situations, they really will know best!

The best adventurers always have their and others' safety topmost in their mind – you must always do that. Some of the activities we describe in this book must only be contemplated as last resorts. In any crisis situation, you should remember to think calmly and act sensibly once you have considered every course of action available to you and after you have tried to seek help and advice. Remember, too, of course, not to break the law, and to show respect and consideration for other people and their property.

To help you prepare for your adventures, we are passing on advice that we have gathered from experts. However, we wanted to share so many things with you that we cannot guarantee that this advice is thorough and complete. It is intended to get you started. In order to be fully prepared for your life as an adventurer, you absolutely must consult professionally trained experts and listen to their advice before taking part in adventurous activities.

We urge you to follow these guidelines and to be the best adventurer you can possibly be!

We are terribly grateful to
Audrey Carangelo, Margaret Conroy and Esra Cafer for
diligently helping us to compile our notes, and to our friends at Dynamo Design
for laying it all out in such a splendid way.

We also wish to thank the good people of Hodder Children's Books for binding our book
so beautifully. We are extremely proud to pass it on to you.

We dedicate this book to Timothy Kirrin, beloved friend

Authors' note: illustrations contained in this book depicting the Famous Five have been supplemented by Julian Kirrin. They were not drawn at the time of the unsolved mystery, but we think they add a wonderful touch to our book. We hope that you enjoy them. (Though Julian would never say so himself, they are really very good!)

You can learn more about our wonderful book at
www.famousfive.co.uk

Contents

Dear Children,

If you're old enough to be reading this book, you're old enough to have your own adventures … and we can help. When we were your age, we had dozens of thrilling adventures. We camped, sailed and trekked; we swam, climbed and explored. And we had a simply *wonderful* time! It's time you knew that we also gained quite a reputation around Kirrin for cracking mysteries, solving crimes and uncovering hidden treasures. (The local police came to depend on us quite a bit.)

There was one mystery that gave us a great deal of trouble to solve – the mystery of the Royal Dragon. Despite our best efforts, this priceless royal heirloom has remained hidden for more than a century. It *is* frustrating when one gets so close to revealing the answer and then … simply runs out of time! And yet, we are sure that all the clues pointing to its location are right here in this book. Now the mystery is for you to solve.

To help you succeed in your mission, we will share with you every clue we uncovered, as well as our diary pages and confidential letters relating to the case. We are also including notes and tips on essential survival techniques and mystery solving skills. If you are to enjoy your own adventures, this knowledge will be invaluable to you.

The documents contained in this book are important. We trust you will guard them well. In fact, we strongly advise it. You should know that there are others who seek the Royal Dragon; descendants of its thief, just as you are descendants of the Famous Five. They are scoundrels, driven by selfish greed. Do not let them find it!

We hope that you can follow our trail and solve this mystery for yourselves, acquiring essential adventuring skills along the way. We also hope that you, like us, will enjoy your own wonderful adventures!

Are you ready? Good luck!

Julian Dick Anne George

In memory of Timmy
The Famous Five

CHAPTER ONE

A Curious Caller

It all started during one of our lovely summer holidays at Kirrin Cottage. The Famous Five were together again and planning a camping holiday in the woods for our last week or two before the start of a new school term. We were excited to bursting! Our woodland holiday would start in just a few days. Then something strange happened that made us change all our plans. Looking back over our diary entries on that fateful day, we feel that George and Dick together have perfectly captured the incident of the curious caller.

From the desk of Georg~~ina~~e Kirrin

August 16th, 1959

Mother and Father had a strange caller stop by the cottage today, a woman reporter. She asked after Henry John Kirrin, my and the cousins' great-great-great-grandfather. She said she was writing a book about old sea captains and was researching Captain HJK and the wrecking of his ship, the Peregrine, somewhere off Land's End about 100 years ago. We were startled by her words, though we know HJK wrecked at least one other ship. That went down right here, by my very own Kirrin Island. The cousins and I found treasure aboard and a box full of the Captain's papers (which I've still got somewhere). Father took the reporter's card and said he would call if he found any of HJK's papers. I'll not be sharing that box with her, that's for certain!

I found the reporter quite odd. She's a tall, waspish woman who wears pearls and the most absurd red, high-heeled shoes. Really! I thought reporters had to chase down a story. In shoes of that sort she couldn't even walk down a story ... and I could tell Timmy didn't care much for her either.

Mother's calling. We've got roast beef and all the trimmings for tea!

BEVERLY BUTLERTON

REPORTER

Telephone: Fleet Street 2691

D.K. 16th August, 1959

A rather peculiar woman came to Kirrin Cottage today. She asked Uncle Quentin and Aunt Fanny about old Captain Kirrin and the ship he lost back in the 1850s. Well, I'm very excited about it! After all, the last time we explored one of the Captain's wrecks, we found a map that led us right to the lost Kirrin treasure! Now we learn that he was captain of another ship that went down!

I say! I wonder what it would be like to be on a ship that's about to sink? Terrifying, I should expect, but thrilling all the same! I must read up on that. One never knows when one will be shipwrecked in the middle of the ocean! I have a peculiar feeling about that reporter.

Good old Julian has drawn a perfect likeness of her, which explains why he was unusually quiet earlier. Anne seems quite taken with the reporter; says it must be fascinating, investigating the past and writing about it. Anne's eyes lit up when Butlerton told her she only ever wears red shoes! Sometimes our Anne can get carried away – she told the reporter about Captain Kirrin's other wreck and the treasure map we children found on board. Miss Butlerton got a funny gleam in her eye then. But that was nothing compared to the scowl old George gave Anne!

I'm going to ask Uncle if I can look at some of his books. I want to find out more about the Peregrine. I wonder if this could be the beginning of another fine adventure?

Julian's original likeness of Beverly Butlerton.

HOW TO SURVIVE A SHIPWRECK

You never think a shipwreck will happen to you! But then there is a terrible crash, jagged rocks breach the hull, water pours in uncontrollably and the Captain gives the order to abandon ship. You scramble for the lifeboats but it's too late – the fathomless ocean is dragging everything down. You only have time to grab a lifejacket and jump! Within a few short minutes your ship has sunk, you're surrounded by debris and floating in shark-infested waters. What do you do?

Did you pay attention to the safety briefing when you boarded the ship? Think back to those instructions! You should have been told:

> How to recognize the emergency alarm signal.
> How to recognize the abandon ship signal.
> How to use your lifejacket.
> The safest ways to leave the ship.

If there is a crew member nearby who is trained in emergency procedures, follow their orders. But if you're surrounded by frantic passengers, it's up to you to take command of the situation!

DON'T PANIC!

> Panicking will waste valuable time and energy.
> Gather all survivors together. There is safety and comfort in numbers.
> Stay calm and keep yourself and others safe until help arrives.

ASSESS THE SITUATION

> Is anyone injured? What treatment is needed? Do you have a first-aid kit?
> Have any lifeboats survived the shipwreck? Can you use any debris to create makeshift rafts?
> What shelter do you have?
> How much food and drink do you have?
> Do you have any way of signalling for help?

SURVIVAL SECRETS

1. **EMERGENCY FIRST AID**
   - > **Wounds**
     Control any bleeding by applying pressure to the wound or to either side of it.
   - > **Hypothermia**
     Try to increase the casualty's temperature by wrapping them in a warm blanket.
   - > **Shock**
     Loosen tight clothing, and lay the casualty down with their head low and their legs raised.
   - > **Concussion**
     Apply a cold compress to any swelling and place the casualty in the recovery position.
     (See page 140 for more information on first aid.)

2. **LIFEBOATS AND RAFTS**
   - > Try to save lifeboats from the ship.
   - > Save as much rope or cord as you can find. You will find many uses for it.
   - > Make rafts by tying barrels, planks of wood or other floating materials together.
   - > Lash your boats or makeshift rafts side by side. It is important to stay together.
   - > Get out of the water as quickly as possible. Swimming or treading water will drain you of precious energy.

3. **FOOD AND DRINK**
   - > Ration supplies carefully in case you are stranded for a long time.
   - > Eat starches and fats but very little protein, to maintain hydration.
   - > Seawater is high in salt and not drinkable. Use a piece of waterproof material (sail canvas or tarpaulin) to funnel rainwater into a container. Wash the material in the sea first to remove any build-up of salt crystals.

4. **SHELTER**
   - > Use debris from the ship to protect you from the elements.
   - > A sail or tarpaulin can give shade from the sun and protect you from the rain and wind.

5. **SIGNALLING FOR HELP**
   - > If you have one, send up a rocket as a distress signal.
   - > It's unlikely, but if anyone has a working mobile phone, dial 999 and ask for the Coastguard.
   - > When help appears, mark your position by letting off an orange smoke or a red flare.
   - > Don't waste flares or smokes by letting them off when there's no boat in sight.

WAITING FOR HELP TO ARRIVE

- > If it's hot, submerge yourself in water every two or three hours. The water on your clothing evaporating will keep you cooler than dry clothes.
- > If it's cold, hold your inner arms close to your chest, press your thighs together and raise them up to your body. Stay still. This helps you retain heat in the areas where you can lose it most quickly.
- > The more you move the more energy you use. Conserve energy and sleep whenever possible.

SHARKS!

- > If sharks begin to circle your group, stay close together and don't panic. Sharks are more likely to attack isolated individuals.
- > Don't allow anyone who is bleeding into the water. Sharks are attracted to blood.
- > Ask everyone to remove shiny, reflective jewellery. To a shark, it may look like fish scales.
- > If a shark attacks, use anything you can to hit its eyes or gills with quick, repeated jabs. It will realize you are not defenceless.

Dick always was the one who loved hunting about for bits of history and facts. True to his word, he approached Uncle Quentin about looking through his old books. Quentin Kirrin, George's father, and uncle to the rest of the Five, was a renowned scientist with an equally renowned temper. As children, we were all rather afraid of his angry outbursts, even our feisty George. One did not want to disturb Quentin Kirrin in the middle of one of his precious experiments. But Dick would not be deterred – and he was successful! On a rainy afternoon, we all gathered to look through the books and uncovered some important clues.

Sometimes, mystery-solving involves poring over musty old volumes of history to turn up forgotten clues. We always approached a puzzle in this way, by exploring all the angles and digging in unlikely places. Julian remembered the reporter saying that the ship had gone down "off Land's End" so he focused his search on the surrounding area. Clever Julian found a reference to the *Peregrine* itself, buried in *A History of British Maritime Disasters, Vol. III, 1850-1899.* What we read told us the rough location of Captain Kirrin's wreck.

The Royal Charter Storm

25-26 October 1859

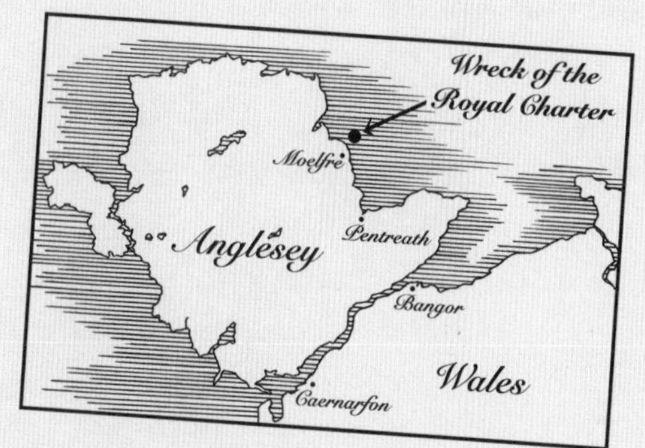

Following several days of unsettled weather things took a turn for the worse on the afternoon of the 25th. A sudden shift in wind direction and an increase in speed began to cause property damage along the south coast. This surge of weather headed north along the Welsh coast wreaking huge amounts of damage as it went. Gale force winds of more than 100 miles per hour and measuring 12 on the Beaufort Scale lashed the coast continuing along the Mersey before heading for Scotland. A definitive account of all losses cannot be compiled due to missing records in many cases. The storm is estimated to have sunk 200 ships with more than 800 lives lost. Noteworthy losses are recorded here.

Ships Name:	Captain:	Location:	Losses:	Survivors:
The Royal Charter	Cpt. V. Taylor	Anglesey	451	41
SS Sheerness	Cpt. C. Aberforth	Cornwall	53	None
SS Gwendoline	Cpt. A. Forster	Portsmouth	50	8
Jakobstad	Cpt. P. Lundstrund	Cornwall	None	58
The Claire-Louise	Cpt. P. Wakeman	Cornwall	100	None
SS Patricia	Cpt. K. Simpson	New Quay	50	300
The Amelia-Jane	Cpt. S. Richards	Liverpool	20	200
HMS Peregrine	Cpt. H. Kirrin	Scilly Isles	13	2
SS Louisa	Cpt. B. Petersen	Liverpool	35	60
Passarvenga	Cpt. O. Knudsen	Liverpool	20	None
The Charlotte	Cpt. D. Tucker	Exeter	None	255
SS Griffin	Cpt. J. Fuller	Dartmouth	27	73
SS Salutaion	Cpt. H. Jameson	Southampton	12	138
Voltaire	Cpt. R. Spinnaker	Exmouth		

It was clear that the treacherous rocks around the Scilly Isles had claimed many fine ships, including the *Peregrine*. Our interest in the Captain's wreck was piqued and we wanted to know more. George agreed to find her box of the Captain's papers later that day and, satisfied, we all set off for a picnic by the seaside. However, Anne was to discover that the box wasn't in George's possession at all – it was in Uncle Quentin's. When Anne told us what she'd learned, we were determined to retrieve the box and explore its contents (we adventurers have an unquenchable thirst for knowledge!). Anne and Julian's diaries tell the story.

Anne's Diary - 17th August, 1959

George's bedroom (which I share during the holidays), Kirrin Cottage

Dear Diary,

A most intriguing thing occurred today! I popped back to the Cottage to get my cardigan, leaving the others on the windy beach and, just as I was on my way out again, I overheard Uncle Quentin in the hall say, "Good day, am I speaking to Miss Butlerton?" He was on the phone to the nice reporter from the other day! Well, I really didn't mean to eavesdrop (for that is a terrible way to behave), but I did so like Miss Butlerton that I wanted to learn whether Uncle would invite her to visit us again. But this is what I heard!

"Miss Butlerton, I've dug up an old box of things that belonged to my great-great-grandfather, Captain Kirrin . . . I'm not entirely sure what's there; some letters I think . . . I have no use for them and wondered if they would be interesting for your research . . . You'll collect them? Good . . . No, not today, I must get back to my experiment and cannot be disturbed . . . Tomorrow is fine. Good day Miss Butlerton."

Well! I ran straight out and told the others. George went white as a sheet, the way she does before exploding into one of her rages. The boys and I were instantly silent.

"That beast!" she cried. (I'm sorry to say that she was talking of her own father. She and Uncle are often cross with one another. Though I'd never dare mention it to George, I can't help but wonder if it's not because they are so similar?) By now, George was red in the face and looking quite livid. "Father's stolen our box!" she cried.

Julian tried to calm her down, explaining that the box belonged as much to Uncle Quentin as it did to us, but George wouldn't hear it.

"Don't you see? I'll bet it's full of clues about the Peregrine. I'll bet that ship is full of treasure, too. And now Father's going to give that box and all its clues to that horrid reporter! Well I'll not let him! I'm going right now to demand he give that box to us! We found it, it's rightfully ours."

George immediately set off to confront Uncle. Oh! I do admire her bravery but I do so hate it when they row. Thank goodness Julian stepped in.

"Now, slow down George. In this state you'll only make Uncle Quentin cross and then we'll never see what's in that box. Let me ask him for it sensibly and politely. We must get those papers. I shall take his supper tray to him this evening and ask him then. Agreed everyone?"

For once, George didn't argue with Julian, knowing that he was right.

We haven't mentioned the Captain's papers all afternoon. Now that supper's only moments away, the others can talk of nothing else! I don't much like hearing about grand old ships all broken up on the rocks, but I do hope Julian can convince Uncle to let us look through that box. Who knows what exciting things we'll find?

The Diary of Julian Kirrin - Kirrin Cottage

17th August, evening

Blow! Uncle Q refused to let me see those papers. He'll give the box to the reporter tomorrow. Dick and I will have to find it tonight, while Uncle's asleep.

18th August, nearly 2 o'clock in the morning

We did it! Shortly after midnight, Dick and I crept into Uncle's study. Timmy stirred, ready to attack any intruder but, seeing us, he kept quiet. We kept the lights off and held our torches under our shirts so there was just enough light to see by, but not enough to show under the door.

Uncle's study is covered with bits of scientific paraphernalia and pages of notes. Dick and I began to examine the room when we heard a sharp woof from Timmy, quickly followed by the sound of footsteps! We both dived behind the couch along the far wall.

Uncle Quentin entered, muttering to himself. He sat at his desk and began writing. Dick looked terrified and I must admit I felt the same as Uncle could be there all night! Luckily for us, he stayed only 20 minutes or so, by which time Dick had fallen sound asleep on the floor! When I gave him a shake he bolted upright, kicking his foot into something hard under the couch.

We looked and found a wide, flat metal box. I recognized it instantly as the box we'd pulled from the wreck at Kirrin Island. Inside were several old letters and the very thing I'd hoped to find – the Peregrine Captain's Log! I left some papers for Uncle to give to the reporter. Uncle Q is so absent-minded, I'm sure he won't remember what the box contained. We took the Logbook, a plan of the Peregrine and a pack of letters with an interesting coat of arms. What a find!

Kirrin Cottage

Thanks to the boys' bravery, we had retrieved the Captain's box from Uncle Quentin's study! We weren't proud of taking the papers by stealth but we didn't see why the reporter should simply be given them all. If you're going to solve mysteries of your own, you'll need to be ready for adventurous late-night missions just like this.

As arranged, the reporter returned to Kirrin Cottage the next day. Anne served her tea (sandwiches, a ham pie, a large fruit cake and a chocolate cake – scrumptious!) and sat with the grown-ups while the rest of us pored over the Captain's papers (we've inserted some of these so you can see for yourself). Anne told us later that the tea had been awkward and that Uncle Quentin had not "been at all kind to jolly Miss Butlerton". The reporter had told Uncle about a legend surrounding the *Peregrine* and its cargo on that fateful voyage.

> *"Stories tell of a valuable treasure on board the ship – a priceless heirloom belonging to the King of Siam which was stolen and brought to England. Rumour has it that the* Peregrine *was charged with returning the treasure before something terrible happened. War or something like that. Oh, and the legend also says that there was a map to help find the treasure. Isn't that an amusing tale? My readers would find that most charming, I'm sure. Did you ever hear about a treasure map in your family, Mr Kirrin?"*

Uncle had become short-tempered and told her that all talk of treasure and legends was poppycock and that he would expect better of a serious journalist from Fleet Street!

The story of a legend was met with quite a different reaction from the Famous Five. We had already discovered the rough location where the *Peregrine* sank and now here was talk that the ship had been carrying a priceless heirloom! We felt sure that the treasure was somewhere on the wreck of the *Peregrine*, hidden in the waters around the Isles of Scilly. It was decided. The Famous Five would not be camping in the woods after all for our holidays. We were going to the Isles of Scilly.

CHAPTER TWO

The Captain's Secrets

Official Bill of Lading

Port of Cardiff

Account states Clipper Peregrine granted permission of departure from the Port of Cardiff bound for Port of Siam on this day 25th October 1859.

Ship and crew declared seaworthy and fit for travel on journey of trade to transport steel.

Port of Siam final port of arrival on or around 5th January 1860

Date:	Description:	Fee:
October 21	Loading of seven bales of Sims Tweed	£4 5s 6d
October 23	Loading of twelve tons of steel	£19 3s 8d
October 24	Loading of personal items for Siam colonists	N/A

Signed

Captain H. J. Kirrin

APPROVED APPROVED

H. Jones

Harbourmaster - Port of Cardiff

HMS PEREGRINE - CLIPPER CLASS

Official Ship's Plan, Specification and History

SPECIFICATION

Nationality:	British
Port:	London
Owner:	Peninsular & Oriental Shipping Company
Service:	London, Cornwall, India, China, Australia, (cargo, mail and passenger service)
Builder:	Messrs Harland & Wolff, Ltd, Belfast
Launched:	January 15, 1850
Maiden voyage:	May 5, 1850
Fate:	Foundered off Isles of Scilly during Royal Charter Storm of 1859. Partial wreck recovery broken up by Metal Industries Limited, Faslane, Scotland
Displacement:	2,000 tons
Length:	198 feet
Beam:	32 feet
Draught:	20 feet
Propulsion:	Sail
Masts:	Three
Speed:	17.5 knots (32 km/h)
Capacity:	1,700 tons
Construction:	Red hull with black boot-topping and stone upperworks
Complement:	20-27 members

SAIL PLAN

1. Foremast
2. Mainmast
3. Mizenmast
4. Flying Jib
5. Outer Jib
6. Inner Jib
7. Fore Course
8. Fore Lower Topsail
9. Fore Upper Topsail
10. Fore Topgallant Sail
11. Fore Royal
12. Main Royal Staysail
13. Main Topmast Staysail
14. Main Skysail
15. Main Royal
16. Main Topgallant Studdingsail
17. Main Topgallant
18. Main Topmast Studdingsail
19. Main Upper Topsail
20. Main Lower Topsail
21. Main Course
22. Mizen Topgallant Staysail
23. Mizen Topmast Staysail
24. Mizen Royal
25. Mizen Topgallant Sail
26. Mizen Upper Topsail
27. Mizen Lower Topsail
28. Mizen Course
29. Spanker

Received
August 5th, 1860
H.J.K.
1
2
3
7
8
9
10
11
12
13
14
15
16
17
18
19
20
21
22
23
24
25
26
27
28
29
B
C
D
E
F
G
BELOW DECK
A. . . . . Dolphin Striker
B. . . . . Ship's Galley
C. . . . . Cargo Hold
D. . . . . Bilge Pump
E. . . . . Sail Locker
F. . . . . Captain's Quarters
G. . . . . Crew Quarters

HMS PEREGRINE  **CAPTAIN'S LOG**

October 24th, 1859

I have sent word to the Honourable Duke of Dibeltoynn confirming that I shall assist with his most vital mission.
The Peregrine is ship-shape and my crew is ready to set sail. We leave tomorrow, despite the dangers of the autumn seas. The Duke is anxious for his cargo to reach Siam forthwith, for the fate of an entire kingdom is at stake. If the cargo is not delivered, there will be a civil war! The Duke informs me that his cargo is eagerly sought by men of ill repute. All our correspondence must be encoded.
The Duke is indeed a clever man. No one would suspect that his letters hold a secret message with quite a different meaning.
Only a decoder can reveal the hidden messages. He has supplied me with the key to cracking his code. I am keeping it right here, in open view, so as not to attract attention to it.

We sail for Siam tomorrow.

H.J.K.

We searched the Captain's papers and found the following letter from the Duke of Dibeltoynn – it *had* to be the one that prompted the Captain's log entry of 24th October, 1859.

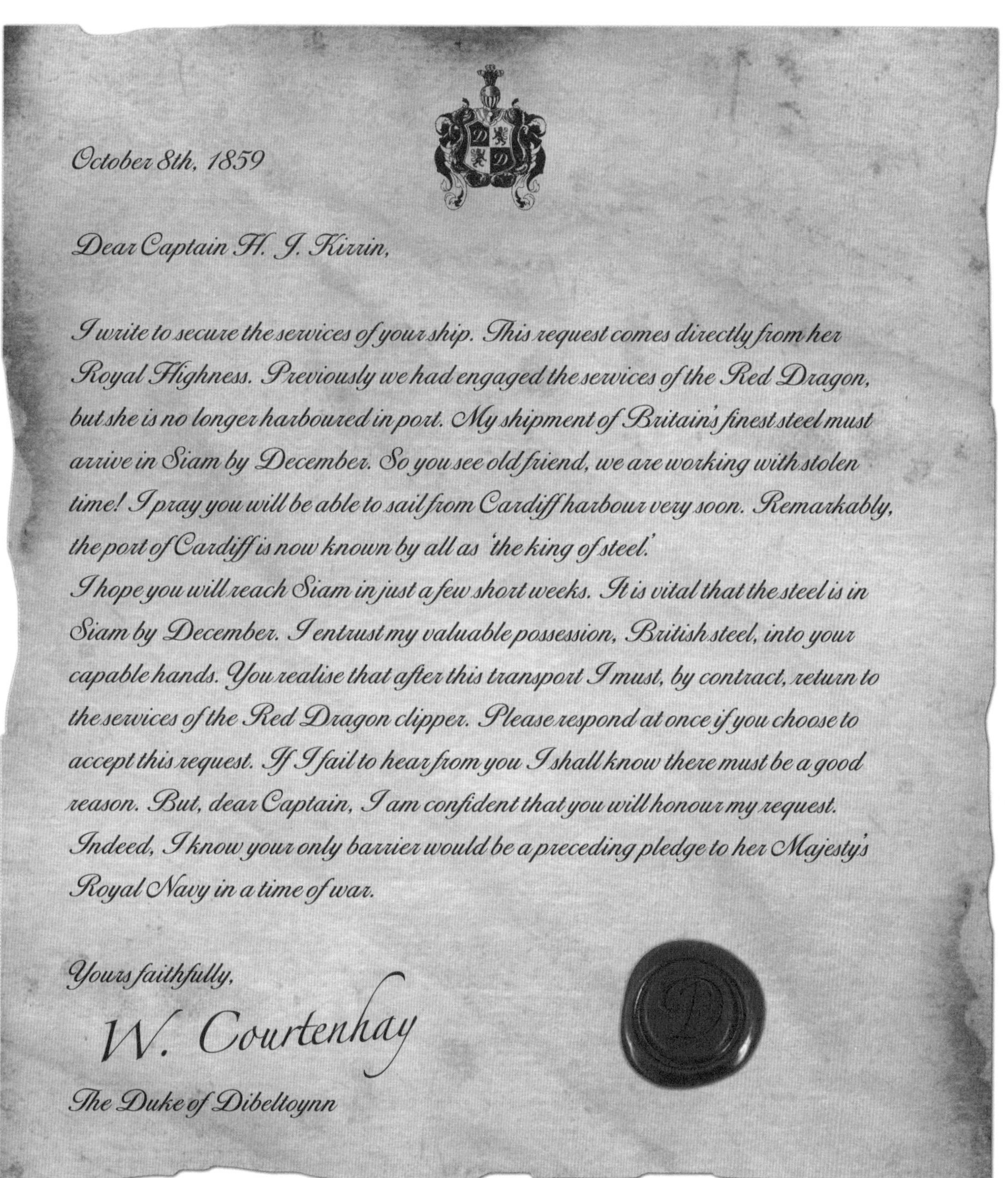

October 8th, 1859

Dear Captain H. J. Kirrin,

I write to secure the services of your ship. This request comes directly from her Royal Highness. Previously we had engaged the services of the Red Dragon, but she is no longer harboured in port. My shipment of Britain's finest steel must arrive in Siam by December. So you see old friend, we are working with stolen time! I pray you will be able to sail from Cardiff harbour very soon. Remarkably, the port of Cardiff is now known by all as 'the king of steel.'
I hope you will reach Siam in just a few short weeks. It is vital that the steel is in Siam by December. I entrust my valuable possession, British steel, into your capable hands. You realise that after this transport I must, by contract, return to the services of the Red Dragon clipper. Please respond at once if you choose to accept this request. If I fail to hear from you I shall know there must be a good reason. But, dear Captain, I am confident that you will honour my request. Indeed, I know your only barrier would be a preceding pledge to her Majesty's Royal Navy in a time of war.

Yours faithfully,

W. Courtenhay

The Duke of Dibeltoynn

We were extremely puzzled after reading the Duke's letter. The Captain's log made it clear that the letter contained a hidden message but we had no way of reading it. What did Captain Kirrin mean by saying he'd hidden the decoder 'right here'? We were fascinated by these words, convinced that the Captain's desk had held the answer – 100 years ago! We had no hope of reading the secret message without it. As it turned out, it was Timmy who found the code reader (Dick later made a copy as it was almost worn through). We'll let George's diary entry from that day explain how it happened.

From the desk of Georg~~ina~~e Kirrin

August 18th, 1959

What an afternoon we've had!

The cousins and I were poring over the Captain's log, wishing we could read the Duke's hidden message, when Timmy bounded in and jumped right on top of me, sending the logbook and the Duke's letter flying across the boys' bedroom, and me into a heap on the floor (I wasn't hurt a bit, of course). Poor Tim! He must have got tired of us being indoors and reading all the time. He was just getting our attention. But the clever thing did more than that!

The log had landed on its front so that when Anne picked it up, she could see for the first time that the back of the book was covered in a series of roughly cut holes. I would never have noticed something like that. The log was old and very worn, so I suggested they were moth holes but Anne got very animated about it.

"Moths don't eat leather," she told me. "These holes were cut on purpose. How strange!"

Just then Dick grabbed the logbook from her hands, crying, "You've got it, Anne!"

He had made an exciting discovery about how to crack the Duke's code!

Anne and Dick were both marvellous, but if it weren't for Timmy, we would never have found the decoder! Good old Tim. The cleverest dog that ever lived, without a doubt!

HOW TO CRACK CODES

Keep your secrets safe

During the course of your investigations secret codes will most likely pop up more than once. Breaking the codes could lead you to cracking a case a lot sooner than you thought, but what are you to do when confronted with what looks a seemingly random jumble of letters? Learning some basic code-making abilities will help you when it comes to breaking them. Let us take you on a beginners guide to codes and help us set you on the right path to becoming a code-master in next to no time.

ROUTE CODE

You will need:
- Two pieces of paper
- Pencil or pen

01. Draw a rectangle on each piece of paper.
02. On each rectangle draw a grid that has five squares across and five squares down.
03. On one piece of paper draw a line through the boxes with a red pen and give this to the person receiving the message. This is known as the route key.
04. Following the line you have drawn write your message on the blank grid on the other piece of paper.
05. The more complicated the line you draw, the harder your message will be to decipher.

Crack it
Look at the route key and follow the path around the letters of the message.

Get Cracking
Using the route key below try to crack the code in the box.

H	E	L	D	W
D	L	O	S	O
N	P	E	T	N
E	T	H	A	E
S	O	T	B	L

Remember that the person receiving the code will need to know the route key you used to write the message, or they will not be able to decipher it.

MASK

You will need:
- Tracing paper
- Pencil

A masked message can only be decoded by using a special overlay of card or paper (called a *mask*) with pieces cut out of it. Without the mask, the message, if it is well written, will appear to be a completely innocent piece of text. For example, in the section below, a coded message is hidden.

If I can learn how to crack a code, anyone can – even you! All it takes is a love of language and the patience to follow a step-by-step method. The first thing to do is figure out what kind of code you are trying to solve. If you have a letter with a secret message hidden in it, then you have the type of code where you must find which words are part of the coded message, and which words are just there to hide the messages.

To crack this code you will need to trace the mask below and lay it over the message. The coded words in the message are revealed through the holes in the mask.

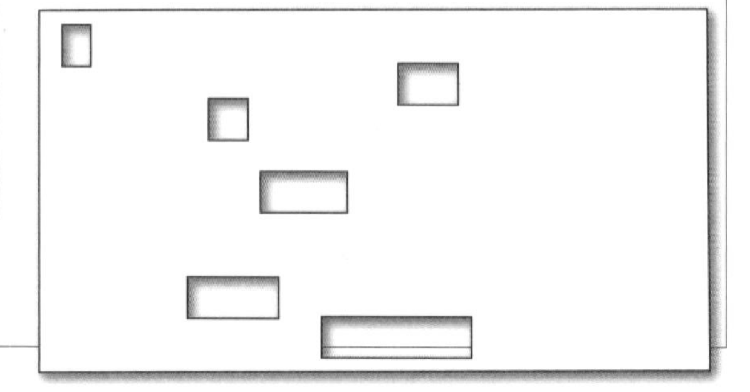

SLIDER CODE

You will need:

- Two sheets of paper
- Scissors
- Pencil or pen

01. Cut a long strip of paper, it should be wide enough so that you are able to write the alphabet backwards twice on one line starting at Z. This will be piece (A).
02. Make a rectangle with the other sheet of paper. It should be three times the height of your alphabet paper and wide enough to be able to write the alphabet once on one line. This will be piece (B).
03. Cut two slots in piece (B). They should be the same height as piece (A) and positioned beneath the beginning and end of the alphabet written on piece (B).
04. The long strip of paper, piece (B), should now be able to fit comfortably in the piece you cut out with the letters clearly visible in the slot.
05. With the two pieces together, choose a key letter from piece (A) and position it underneath the letter *A* on piece (B).
06. The letter you have chosen will be your codekey. You must let the receiver of the message know the codekey.
07. To write your message in code, select the letters of the message on piece (B). Look what letter appears below each on piece (A), and write those down to put the letters into code.

Crack it.

To read the message, place the code key letter on piece (A) underneath the letter *A* on piece (B). Select the letters of the coded message on piece (A), and write down the matching letter above from piece (B). This will give you the decoded message.

Get Cracking!

Use the slider code to decipher the message below using the codekey of H.

OAD XDJ ZP NUEDQ OAD VHO

RULER CODE

You will need:

- Paper
- Ruler
- Pencil or pen

01. Lay a ruler across a sheet of paper and write the letters of your message at every centimetre mark.
02. Make a mark on the last letter of your message. Either circle the letter or mark a line underneath it. Tell the reader which is the last letter of your message.
03. Between the letters of your message fill in other letters. You can either make words or use random letters to make your message completely hidden.

Crack it

To read the message, place a ruler under the letters. Make sure that the final letter is over a centimetre mark. Now read the letters that appear at every centimetre mark.

Get Cracking!

Use the ruler code to decipher the message below.

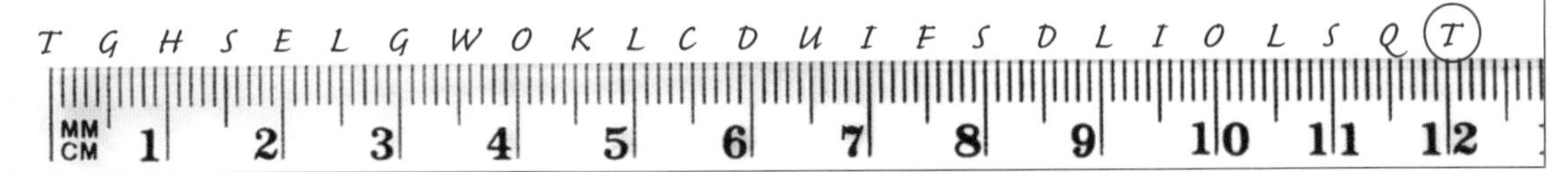

CODE TYPE: CIPHERS

A tried and tested secrecy system

For hundreds of years ciphers have been used to hide information from prying eyes. Since before the times of the ancient Romans, information has been hidden in all manner of variations of the cipher, with probably the most recent and well known being the Enigma machines of World War II. Once you've learned the basics of ciphers it's simple to make up your own.

A cipher is a coded message where certain letters are substituted for others – making the secret message look like nonsense. For example;

QBYLY CM NBY NLYUMOLY GUJ?

Here's how to crack this cipher:

01. Write the alphabet in a line across your page. You will use this as your tally sheet to keep track of the parts of the cipher you have uncovered.

02. Make a note of how many times each letter is used in the cipher. Like this:

QBYLY CM NBY NLYUMOLY GUJ?

A	B	C	D	E	F	G	H	I	J	K	L	M	N	O	P	Q	R	S	T	U	V	W	X	Y	Z
	2	1				1			1		3	2	2	1		1								5	

03. The letter Y is used 5 times, The letter L is used 3 times, and so on. You may not know it, but the letters E, T, O and A are found in words more often than any other letters. Look at your alphabet tally. The letter that is used most often in the cipher is Y.

04. Try substituting E, T, O, or A for the letter Y. You can make a good guess that the letter Y probably stands for the letter E in the cipher. It is the most plausible possibility:

COMMON WORDS

Now, take a look at the words in the cipher. Some of the words only have two or three letters. There are some very common two and three-letter words. One of these words is likely to fit the cipher:

Common 2-Letter Words	Common 3-Letter Words
as, is, it, me, of, in, he	the, his, why, not, are, you

05. Look at the third word in the cipher. It has an E at the end, so the word is most likely to be THE. Once you've written 'THE' into the cipher, you've learned two more letters. Now you know that N in the cipher stands for T and that B stands for H. Now, substitute T for N, then H for B in the cipher.

06. Look at the first word in the message. What words are spelled __ H E __ E? The word could be THERE or WHERE.
07. Look closely. The cipher has a question mark at the end. The word WHERE asks a question.
08. Put WHERE into the cipher. Now what further letters are revealed? Q in the cipher stands for W, and L stands for R. Substitute these letters just like you did in the previous steps.

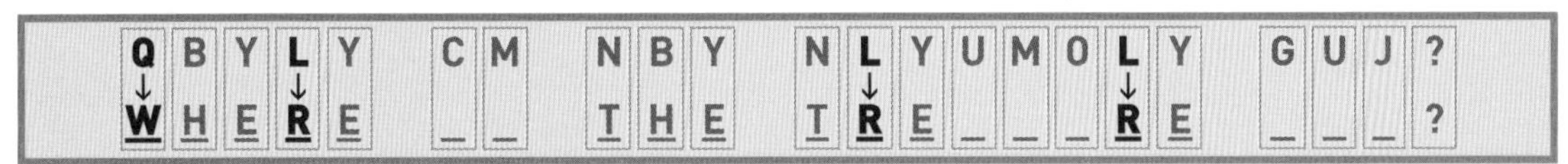

09. You can see that letter-by-letter you are cracking the cipher. Read the message. WHERE __ __ THE TRE__ __ __RE __ __ __ ?"
10. Look at the second word. What two-letter word might fit there? You can make a good guess that the second word will be IS. Write IS in the cipher and substitute any letters you new learn.

11. Look hard at the fourth word TRE _ S _ RE. Say it out loud. It sounds a lot like the word TREASURE, doesn't it? The word makes sense in the cipher! Write TREASURE in the cipher and substitute any new letters you learn.

12. One word left to decipher! The word has an A in the middle. What word can it be? Cat, can, nap, map? What makes sense? MAP of course! You've cracked the cipher.

Try cracking this cipher on your own: OLSC WOLEL PV H WEHC!

_ _ _ _   _ _ _ _ _   _ _   _   _ _ _ _ _

Now that you know how to crack codes you're ready to read the secret message hidden in the Duke's letter. We've left a copy of the code reader among our papers. It looks like an old piece of card and is full of holes. Place it on to the Duke's letter and you'll be able to read the secret message for yourself. Your new-found code-cracking skills will be essential in solving the mystery of the Royal Dragon.

Once we were able to read the Duke's coded message we knew for certain that there had been treasure in the *Peregrine's* cargo. Instead of British steel, the *Peregrine* was secretly carrying something called the Royal Dragon of Siam – that did sound grand!

Anxious to know more about the *Peregrine's* voyage and the fate of the Royal Dragon, we hastily turned to the ship's log. (You should, too.) What we found there answered some of our questions about what actually happened to Captain Kirrin's ship.

HMS PEREGRINE  **CAPTAIN'S LOG**

October 25th, 1859

Second afternoon watch - The gale-force winds and stormy seas are the worst I've seen off the coast in all my years. The Peregrine has been blown off course. We'll not be able to make it around Land's End. I fear that the ship has been blown into the treacherous Isles of Scilly!

First evening watch - The darkness, rain and crashing waves make it impossible to see past the bow of the ship but a short distance. I'm guiding her nearly blind through this wretched storm. A guide light from shore has been spotted. I'm fixing our bearing to its safe beacon.

H.J.K

October 26th, 1859

The Peregrine is no more!
She was lost on the jagged rocks off one of the outer Isles. I stayed aboard until the water covered her decks. I just had time to grab the log and tuck it into my coat. The suction of the ship's sinking dragged me down after her. It was all I could do to hold my breath and struggle to the surface! I made it to the surf's edge but was bruised and cut terribly on the sharp rocks. By the graces, I managed to make it ashore. I'm afraid I can't say the same for my crew. To my horror, many of my men did not make it safely to land this cruel and horrible night.

H.J.K

Goodness! Our great-great-great-grandfather had sailed his ship straight into the worst storm of the 19th century. It seemed strange that the guide light he spotted had steered him directly into the treacherous waters surrounding the Scilly Isles. From what we'd read, those waters were notorious for wrecking ships and all sailors of the day avoided them. It was stranger still to think that if Henry John Kirrin had died that day, the Famous Five would never have existed.

We five were so excited by what we'd found. We felt convinced that the Royal Dragon must be a very valuable piece of treasure: after all, it belonged to a king! And, if the rest of Butlerton's story was to be believed, this royal heirloom was so precious that it had caused a civil war. The Royal Dragon might be lying at the bottom of the sea this very minute. Waiting for the Famous Five to uncover it!

The Diary of Julian Kirrin - *Kirrin Cottage*

18th August, morning

We're going to the Isles of Scilly for our last fortnight of holiday! I've just agreed it all with Aunt Fanny and Uncle Quentin. Turns out that Uncle is leaving for Penzance in two days' time for a science fair and we are to accompany him that far. Penzance is right on the tip of Cornwall and from there we can take a short ferry-ride directly to the Scilly Isles! My research shows that there are dozens of islands but people live on only a few of them – most of them are completely deserted. Once we're there, the Five will be able to get off on our own and find the Peregrine. We'll also have some fun camping out and exploring the area of course!

I must start planning immediately. I'll need train and ferry timetables so that I can work out our itinerary. Packing all the gear we'll need is the most important thing. Lots to do!

EAST-WESTERN
TRAIN and FERRY
SERVICES
Between
LONDON - CORNWALL
and the ISLES OF SCILLY
BY ALL ROUTES
From 1st JUNE to 31st DECEMBER 1959
(or until further notice)
A 256874
A 256875

Very useful! Remember to keep for guide Julian

PACK YOUR BAGS FOR ADVENTURE!

Be prepared for anything

You've been offered the trip of a lifetime. You only have half an hour to pack your bag, and you need to be prepared for any eventuality. What do you do?

DECIDE WHAT SIZE OF BACKPACK YOU NEED TO TAKE:

DAY PACK

The smallest bag, ideal for sports kit or an overnight trip where you don't need to carry much.

TRAVEL PACK

For multi-day trips and hikes, available in a variety of colours, sizes and styles, depending on your needs.

EXPEDITION PACK

The largest pack. Used for much longer trips or hikes where you might need extra or specialised equipment.

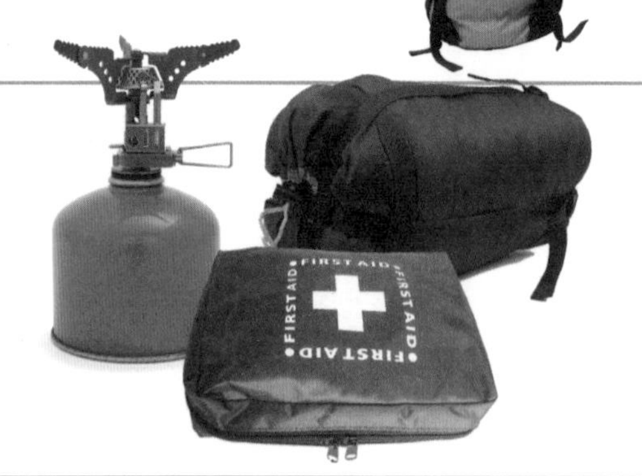

Keep warm and dry

01. **Tent**
    For overnight trips where you will be sleeping outside, a tent is essential to protect you from the elements.
02. **Sleeping bag**
    Put this in a waterproof compression sack to keep it dry and reduce its size.
03. **Rainproof clothes**
    Make sure your waterproof clothing is easily reachable in case of a sudden downpour.
04. **Warm clothing**
    Keep at least a warm jumper and spare pair of trousers within easy reach, the rest can be buried further down in your pack.

Supplies

01. **Snacks**
    Keep snacks and energy bars in a separate daypack, or a pocket, so they are easy to reach as needed.
02. **Food**
    Food other than snacks can be packed further down your pack – but make sure you don't squash it!
03. **Water**
    Keep a bottle of water in easy reach so you don't have to remove your pack each time you want a drink.
04. **Cooking utensils**
    Camp stove, knife, fork, spoon, lightweight plate and cup. Make sure they are packed away clean and kept away from muddy clothes or dirty equipment.
05. **Fuel**
    Make sure the fuel for your stove is properly stored and packed away from anything it could contaminate – particularly food!

Stay safe

01. **First aid kit**
    (See page 44 for what it should contain.)
02. **Torch**
    This will allow you to see where you're going at night, or in dark forests.

03. **Water purification tablets**
    Chemical tablets are available from most outdoor supply shops and can be used for cleaning drinking water. You never know if the water you find on the trail is safe to drink.
04. **Phone**
    A very useful survival tool – excellent for summoning help if lost, and for keeping in touch with other team members if they become separated. Make sure it is fully charged before starting your adventure and bear in mind that the signal may not be 100% in your location– particularly in the wild.
05. **Insect repellent**
    Helps to avoid itchy bites that may become infected, and to keep buzzing pests away.

Which way?

- **Maps**
  Local maps can prove essential, and are well-worth investing in.
- **Compass**
  Even the most basic adventure trip should not start before you have a compass and are comfortable using it. (See page 82 for how to use it.)
- **Important numbers**
  Take a list of local campsites and amenities as well as local emergency services.
- **Clues**
  You will probably need to refer to the clue that led you to this trip to make sure you are heading in the right direction!

What have you forgotten?

01. **Toolkit**
    - Tent repair kit
    - Swiss Army knife
    - Needle, thread and safety pins
    - Spare buttons for your clothing
    - Spare batteries for your torch

02. **Wash Kit**
    - Toothbrush, toothpaste, soap, toilet paper, deodorant

WHAT GOES WHERE?

Insect repellent – near top

Waterproofs – at the top of the pack

First aid kit – at the top of the pack

Tool kit – middle to top

Wash kit – middle to top

Sleeping bag – in centre, of back of pack

Food – in the middle, but not being squashed

Camping stove, and eating utensils – deeper in bag

Cooking stove fuel – in a separate pocket, away from food!

Travel wash – anywhere there is room

Sewing kit – anywhere there is room

Warm clothes – near the bottom except jumper at the top

Tent – attached to straps underneath backpack

FIRST AID KIT

As an adventurer, you should always carry a first aid kit with you for dealing with those unforeseen events. But what do you put in your kit, and why?

PLASTERS - WATERPROOF AND STANDARD

Carry a range of sizes, to cover every eventuality. Plasters can also be used for securing small bandages.

TRIANGULAR BANDAGE

Designed for creating slings for broken or injured limbs. The triangular bandage can be folded into a number of shapes for many different uses.

BANDAGES

Bandage material can be used for holding dressings in place, keeping body parts from moving and securing splints for broken limbs.

TWEEZERS

Ideal for removing splinters, small pieces of gravel - and any other foreign objects - from injuries.

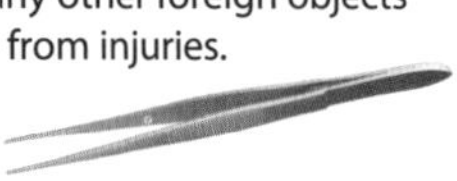

DRESSINGS

Some injuries will need a dressing to help stem blood-flow and protect the wound. Apply the dressing directly to a wound and secure with a bandage.

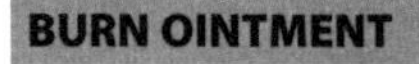

BURN OINTMENT

Used for those little campfire mishaps! It can help relieve pain and inflammation.

ANTISEPTIC WIPES

Can be used to sterilise hands before treating injuries. They can also be used on injuries to help prevent infection.

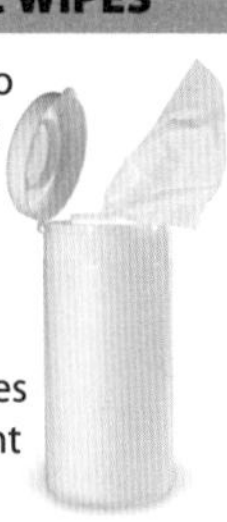

SMALL SCISSORS

Can be used for removing clothing and trimming down bandages, dressings, etc.

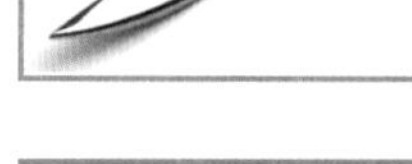

SAFETY PINS

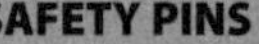

For securing bandages. Ensure these are stored properly closed to avoid pricking your fingers.

LATEX GLOVES

You should wear these to help prevent the spread of infection while cleaning and dressing wounds.

ANTISEPTIC OINTMENT

Can be applied to wounds to help stop infection. Can also give minor pain relief.

MEDICAL ADHESIVE TAPE

Used for securing bandages, plasters and splints.

Food and Supplies

No traveller should be without basic food and supplies. Of course it all depends on how long your trip is going to be and the facilities that will be available to you. There are some general items that every camper will want to take with them, and then there are those special little treats that each individual will want to make sure they have tucked away in their rucksack. Here are a few suggestions to get you started. And remember to always take at least one meal more than you will need in case of emergencies.

Energy is important

With the amount of physical exertion used during camping and backpacking, all food should not only be healthy but also able to provide you with plenty of energy. Your food pack should offer both short-term and long term energy options. Short term energy food is high in carbohydrates, sugars and starch, e.g. crackers, cereal

and pasta. Longer term energy can be gained from foods high in protein and fat such as meat, cheese, eggs and nuts. Of course there's always room for treats that can give a much-needed boost to a flagging traveller! These include dried fruit, sweets and energy bars.

Main Meals

Oats – Use dried milk to make a healthy and filling porridge. Try adding dried fruit and honey for extra flavour.
Bacon / Sausages – What would life be without a good bacon or sausage butty to start the day? Keep these in your cool bag to stop them going off and eat early on in your trip.
Eggs – A good source of protein. Take dried eggs if you are worried about breaking them during travelling.
Bagels – A long-life replacement for bread that can be used in a variety of ways.
Crackers – Light to carry high-energy food that can be spruced up with cheese or any other topping.
Dried soups – Simply add boiling water from your campfire.
Tinned tuna – High in energy and easy to carry.
Tortilla wraps – Fill with tuna and mayonnaise or any other ingredients for a filling snack.
Dried mash – A hearty end to the day with the simple addition of dried milk and boiling water. Try adding cheese and herbs for an extra treat.
Dried Pasta / Rice / Noodles – Simple to use and a good base for lots of dishes that will provide plenty of energy.
Vegetables – Fill a freezer bag with carrot sticks and celery. Long lasting and great as a snack or addition to a meal.

Snack Tips

Backpacking can use a lot of energy, and make you sweat so losing vital salt. Energy bars from camping stores are a good option, as are boiled sweets. Why not try making up your own snack mix to eat on the journey? Fill a bag with sugar-coated chocolate, raisins and nuts. This handy little bag can serve a dual purpose of providing handfuls of goodies to munch on while walking or to be added to porridge and other dishes, to add interest to bland meals. Of course, a solid staple that no traveller can be without is a good old lump of Kendal Mint Cake!

Other Supplies

Fruit – Dried and fresh, for snacking and cooking.
Bread – A good way to bulk out any meal.
Condiment packets – Available from wholesalers or fast food restaurants.
Water – Only carry this heavy item if you are sure there will be no available clean water on your trip.
Cheese – Keep away from sunlight to preserve, it's a great source of protein.
Powdered milk – A must have for adding flavour and texture to a wide variety of dishes.
Tea / Coffee / Hot chocolate – There's nothing like a warm drink to get you going on a chilly morning, or evening.
Foil – Easily overlooked, but exceedingly useful for an array of cooking uses.
Herbs – Seal them in freezer bags and remember a little goes a long way so you won't have to carry much!
Cooking oil – Keep in a sealed container inside a closed bag to avoid spillage.

We were extremely excited about our mystery-adventure holiday. We would be on our own enjoying the brisk sea air, hiking and exploring, swimming and having a grand time.

We loved being on our own, just the Five. Of course, being self-reliant means being prepared. We learned over the course of our many outings just what to take to be ready for any adventure.

It was very late in the evening when we finally finished our packing. We had an early start the next morning but the excitement of what lay ahead kept us all awake. There would be camping, shipwrecks to find and islands to explore. A real adventure – just what the Famous Five like in a holiday!

Chapter Three

The Adventure Begins

On the morning of 19th August, 1959, after a delicious breakfast of porridge with cream, eggs, bacon and toast, we gathered at the railway station, packed and ready for adventure. We all felt a little tired for having stayed up so late into the night, but despite our sleepiness we were full of excitement. Soon we would be on the Isles of Scilly and one step closer to learning what had happened to the Royal Dragon of Siam.

Our luggage loaded, Uncle Quentin ushered us on to the Penzance train. We dared not discuss the real reason for our trip as it made Uncle quite cross to hear about lost treasure and things. We also had to keep the Captain's papers out of his sight, so we couldn't continue searching them for clues.

Julian happily described the trip we would take from Penzance to St Agnes (the island we had decided to visit first while we searched for the exact location of the *Peregrine*). Julian was able to recall the exact times of every train and ferry we would need to catch, without having to look once at his timetables! Julian has always had a near-photographic memory and still surprises us by calling to mind the smallest details about the things he's seen. When he'd finished showing off (he still does that, a little!), he suggested we play some games specifically designed to develop a first-rate photographic memory. Although we were never able to best Julian in these games, our memories certainly did improve.

This is a useful skill to develop if you want to be really good at sleuthing. You never know when you might find yourself without pen or paper and having to remember the licence plate of a kidnapper's car, or having to memorize a treasure map before it burns on an open flame ...

IMPROVE YOUR MEMORY

Train your brain

It can all go very wrong during an investigation if you can't remember vital clues, directions or information. There are many ways you can train your brain to remember important information. Here are just a few to get you going.

BASIC TRAINING

- Stay positive. If you believe that you have a bad memory your brain will subconsciously do everything to prove you right.

- Eat well. The brain is like any muscle and as well as regular work also needs plenty of food to keep it healthy. A well-balanced diet will help to do this.

- Take your time. Information will stay with you a lot longer if you take time to digest and repeat the thing that you are trying to remember.

- Vary your routine. Don't force yourself to sit down at the same time every day and try to study. Variation will help to keep your brain active and stop it getting into a rut.

TECHNIQUES

The Room

There are two 'room' techniques that can be used. One is to create a room in your mind. On the walls are paintings of all the things you wish to remember. In your mind take a stroll around the room pausing to look at each of the paintings and remember their location in the room. When the time comes to recall the information, you'll be able to go straight to your imaginary room and find the relevant paintings.

The other use for the 'room technique' is to picture a room you are familiar with, your bedroom for example. In your mind walk around this room and imagine all the items you need to remember in familiar places. Taking a shopping list as an example; you walk into your room, turn left and see a large chicken sitting on your bed. Continue round the room to see a cow next to your bed, and a mountain of huge sugar cubes sitting on your duvet. This should remind you that you need chicken, milk and sugar. Try it yourself with your own lists and rooms.

Visual Memory

For some people, memories are retained better if they are stored as images. In a similar way to the room technique try taking a virtual snapshot in your head of the person, item or piece of information you are trying to retain. Another option is to create a story using these images.

For example, if you're trying to remember a random list like door, flower and a girl named Rachel, try turning these into a mental photo of a girl wearing a nametag and a floral dress opening a door.

Vivid Association

Vivid association takes visual memory a step further. The brain finds it easier to remember extremes than the general and mundane. Try to link things in your head with extremities such as puns on people's names, over the top actions and situations.

For example, imagine you are trying to remember a person called Pat. This could be done by imagining Pat as a mat on the floor with his face peering out. This will then trigger the memory of 'Pat the mat'. Can't remember where you put your front door keys? Then next time you put them on the table, imagine them melting through the tabletop. Now when you try to recall where you put your keys you'll see them in your mind melting through the table and remember their location. Any type of image or idea can be remembered this way, just make it as out of the ordinary as possible, and it will stick in your mind more easily.

TEST YOUR MEMORY

Increase your brain power

It's always useful to keep your memory active and sharp – you never know when you'll be called upon to remember a secret code, password or complicated directions. Here are a few simple tests to help you practise and keep your memory as sharp as a pin.

- Cover the questions without reading them, then look at the pictures below for two minutes.
- Then cover them up with a sheet of paper.
- How many of the test questions can you answer correctly?
- If you want to make it harder, you and your friends can test each other with your own questions, while the pictures are covered up!

TEST TIME!

01. What time is it on the clock?
02. What colour are the girl's eyes?
03. What colour is the rollercoaster?
04. What picture appears to the left of the penguins?
05. How many windows can you see on the house?
06. How many penguins can you see?
07. In the picture of the fruit and veg how many radishes can you see?
08. What colour are the stripes on the boy's shirt?
09. What direction is the red arrow on the compass pointing?
10. What colour is the motorbike?
11. List all the pictures.

Growing restless, George said she was off to take a closer look at the train's engine and that Timmy was to stay with us. (Tim had of course jumped up to follow his mistress straight away.) The rest of us told her to be sure to bring some snacks back on her return, and continued with our games. The next thing we knew, our train had arrived in Penzance and Uncle Quentin was hurrying us to collect our bags and alight at the station.

"You two get the bags together," said Julian. "I'll go and drag George away from the steam engine. She never did come back with those snacks ..."

Julian went off to find George while Dick and Anne followed Uncle Quentin to the luggage compartment. Ten minutes later, we had made two shocking discoveries: our bags were not where we had left them, or anywhere else in the luggage van; and George was nowhere to be found on the train!

The next hour was very unpleasant. We were stuck in Penzance with none of our carefully packed bags, George missing and a very angry Uncle Quentin. Several porters, and a distraught Timmy, searched the train from top to bottom, and they did find our bags, but not George. When a porter informed Uncle that our bags had been "stashed in the out of order lavatory", he looked accusingly at all three of us, but we knew that we had left them tidily in the luggage van. It was most perplexing. More perplexing still was that the bags had obviously been searched through!

Finally, the train would be held up no longer and departed Penzance, leaving us to wonder whether George had simply vanished into thin air. We were just getting ready to go to the police station and file an official missing persons report, when Timmy started barking loudly and excitedly. There was old George, hiking up to the train platform, looking tired and dirty but with an enormous grin on her face. When she told Uncle Quentin that she had "accidentally fallen off the train" and was "awfully sorry" about the trouble she had caused, the rest of us Five knew that something very strange had happened to George on that train ...

From the desk of Georg~~ina~~e Kirrin

August 19th, 1959

The others were bursting with curiosity to hear what happened to me today but I couldn't say anything while Father was around. I'm going to set it down here, just as I told it to the others, while it's fresh in my mind. I don't want to forget this day for as long as I live!

I left the others playing games to explore the train a little and hopefully get a look at the steam engine itself – I can't bear sitting still for too long. I made my way to the rear of the train, where I found a door marked 'Guard' that was slightly ajar. I knocked but got no reply so I put my head around the door and called out. Instead of the guard, I saw someone (I think it was a woman but things happened so quickly that I can't be certain) searching through our bags. What cheek!

(Julian asked me afterwards how I could be sure that they were our bags and I told him: I recognized the flowers that Anne has sewn onto her blue bag, and I'd know my own bag anywhere, it's red and faded with Timmy's bites and scratches all over it. They were absolutely, certainly, without a doubt our bags!)

"Hey, you!" I cried out, just as someone else grabbed me from behind! I'm sure that was a man because he was awfully strong and rough with me.

Before I could even kick out at him, he held a funny-smelling handkerchief to my mouth and I'm sorry to say that I passed out. (Julian says I mustn't feel badly about it – he's sure that handkerchief was soaked in chloroform.)

When I came to, I was blindfolded, with my feet bound and hands tied behind my back! I didn't tell the others, but I panicked rather and started thrashing about wildly. I'm glad I did, though, because I noticed that the rope around my wrists had some slack in it – whoever had tied me up can't have been very good at knots! I kept moving my wrists and the rope shifted, becoming looser. I hooked a finger around the loose rope, tugging and pulling until my wrists were free. I took off the blindfold, untied my legs and looked around. I was in a small cupboard behind a large stack of boxes and the train was moving slowly ...

HOW TO ESCAPE FROM ROPE BINDS

George's daring escape has made me decide to note down some handy tips and tricks for escaping from ropes, should any of us ever find ourselves in such a predicament!

THINK AHEAD

1. Make your body as big as possible by swelling out your chest.
2. If your upper body is being bound, hold your arms as far from your body as you can without giving your intentions away.
3. If your wrists are being tied together, hold them slightly apart and clench your fists to make your hands and wrists thicker.

KEEP CALM AND STAY ALERT

When your captors aren't watching, relax your body and start wriggling free:

1. Start with your hands and wrists. When they are free the rest of the ropes will be easier to work on.
2. Find the loosest knot and try to loosen it even more, then hook a finger or toe into it and untie the knot.

HINTS AND TIPS

A few things to bear in mind when trying to escape:

- The longer the length of rope that is used, the more stretch it will have.
- People tend to get sloppy when they have to tie a lot of knots. They may leave later knots looser than their earlier ones.
- Become an expert on ropes and knots (like our George!). If you understand how knots are tied, you'll have a much better chance of being able to untie them.

Know the Ropes

You never know when you might need to tie a safe knot - especially with the sort of scrapes we get into! I shall copy some basic instructions into my notebook, so that all of us can learn to tie strong, sturdy knots.

Overhand Knot

This is an excellent starting point for many other knots. The overhand knot is useful as a temporary stopper at the end of a rope to stop it pulling through a ring or pulley.

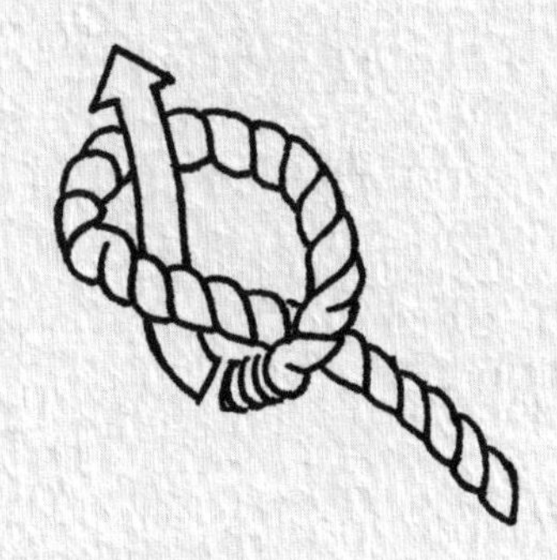

Figure-eight Knot

The figure-eight knot is a more stable stopper knot than the overhand. It is also easier to untie after use. The figure-eight can also be used to join two ropes of the same type together.

Reef (Square) Knot

The reef knot is good for joining two pieces of rope of the same thickness together so the knot does not slip. However, if you use different sized ropes the knot can slip.

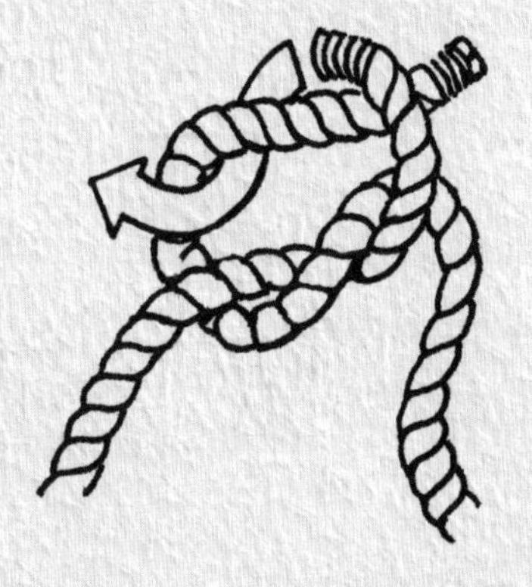

Sheet (Beckett) Bend

This is a much stronger knot than the reef knot. It is good for joining ropes of different sizes, and it can be easily untied, even when wet. It is ideal for hanging light weights, but is not good for climbing.

Carrick Bend

The carrick bend is a very strong knot, but it is easy to undo even if it has been pulled very tight. Ideal for joining larger stiff ropes and easy to untie even when wet.

Bowline

The bowline is ideal for making loops, either along a rope or at the end. The bowline knot is strong and easy to undo, but it can slip when used with synthetic ropes. It is best used with natural fibre ropes.

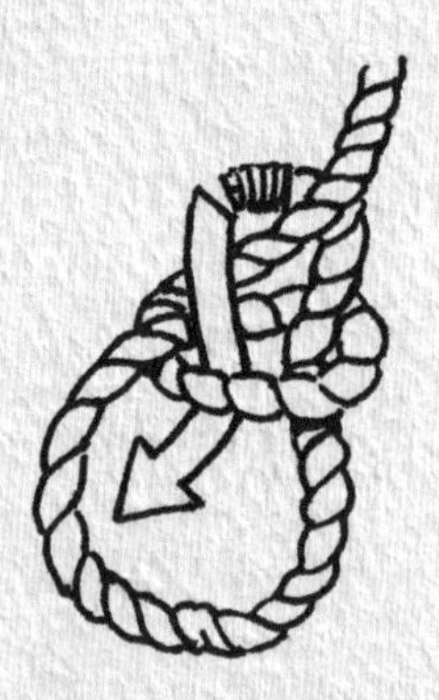

Clove Hitch

The clove hitch is an excellent general securing knot for temporary use. The knot will only tighten when it is pulled at both ends. The clove hitch becomes stronger the harder it is pulled at both ends.

Timber Hitch

The timber hitch is a good knot for hauling logs or pulling heavy items. Up to eight loops can be made around the rope. This gives more strength to the knot.

Taut-Line Hitch

The taut-line is an extremely handy knot, it is useful for tying down tent lines because it can be tightened and loosened quickly. It also makes an excellent climbing safety device. The knot allows the climber to slide the knot up and down the line, but will also go taut if the climber slips, offering an effective safety brake.

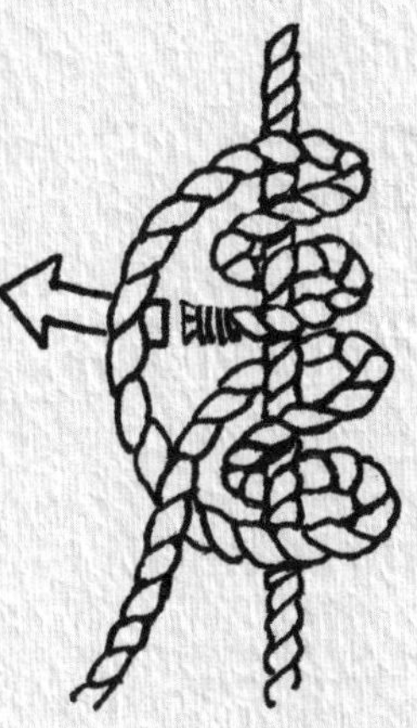

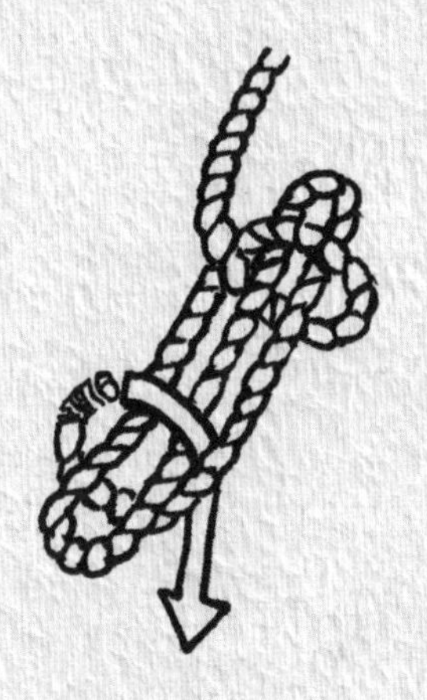

Sheepshank

The sheepshank is useful when your rope is too long for the job at hand but you don't want to cut it. This knot can also bypass weak or damaged parts of your rope. It is excellent under strain and can be simply shaken loose.

From the desk of Georg~~ina~~e Kirrin

August 19th, 1959

I got to my feet and tried the door – it was unlocked! These stupid villains must think children are helpless. I crept out and back towards our carriage. Then I heard the guard calling, 'Next stop St Ives.' St Ives was after Penzance! I'd missed our stop!

Well, there was simply nothing else for me to do. I daren't wait to get off at St Ives in case those stupid villains turned up again so I had to get off the train right then and there, whilst it was moving slowly. When I make up my mind about something, I simply must get on and do it – even if it's frightening (in fact, especially if it is frightening!).

I went to the nearest door and pushed it open. Although the train was moving quite slowly, the ground beneath me seemed to be moving very fast! I took a deep breath and looked at the ground more closely. It was thick with grass and there were no large stones or scratchy bushes around. Not a bad place to jump – so I did. I crouched down low and leapt off, making sure to roll over when I hit the ground. I checked for broken bones (none!), so I turned away from the train and followed the track back to Penzance.

Hurrah! What a thrilling day! Julian and Dick both think I'm awfully brave. Poor Anne, she's so shaken by the very thought of jumping from a moving train. I can't say I'm in a hurry to do it again, that's for certain.

Anne called me her hero! What do you think of that? I didn't want to say anything in front of her, but it seems to me that someone is determined to keep us from arriving in Scilly. It must have something to do with the Royal Dragon of Siam. We've found ourselves another fine mystery! I'm too excited for words!

Julian, George could have done with this information. Very Important! Dick

NEVER JUMP FROM A MOVING TRAIN...

. . . unless the train you are travelling on is headed for certain disaster, and you would be in more danger if you stay on board. If you have no other choice and you must jump, remember these important points.

01. Fast-moving objects (like a person leaping from a moving train) will impact (i.e. hit) the ground with great force.

02. To minimise your impact, jump when the train is moving at its slowest. Wait until it is going around a bend or moving up a hill.

03. No matter how slowly the train is going, you will hit the ground hard. Before you jump, pad your elbows and knees with extra clothes.

04. Before you jump, look at the ground below you. Wait for a soft, grassy stretch of ground. DO NOT jump where there are large rocks, poles, trees or other tracks. You could be badly injured or electrocuted.

05. The biggest danger is that of being run over by the train itself. Crouch down low and leap out as far as possible from the train.

06. Protect your head with your hands and arms. Leap low with your body stretched out to its full length. This spreads the impact along your whole body. Landing on your feet or bottom could leave you with broken bones.

07. When you hit the ground, roll like a log. This helps to lessen the impact of your fall.

NEVER JUMP FROM A MOVING TRAIN unless you have no choice and the train is travelling at a **low speed** in **suitable surroundings**. You could be killed or, at the very least, break your bones!

We knew that George's kidnapping and the robbery of our bags were connected. It *had* to mean that someone didn't want us to get to the Isles of Scilly. But why? We hadn't told anyone of our plans to search for the Captain's wreck or the long-lost treasure it was rumoured to be carrying when it sank. We talked about it well into the night, and it wasn't until the next day that one of us found the answer to this most puzzling question.

The Diary of Julian Kirrin - Penzance

20th August, morning

The mystery of the Royal Dragon deepens! The Five have talked and talked about everything that happened to George yesterday. Why would someone want to keep us from our journey? How indeed could anyone even know what we are planning? Well, I have discovered something very important – it concerns Anne. Last night, just before bedtime, I finally had a chance to speak to Anne alone. (We are staying at a comfortable cottage with a professor friend of Uncle's and his wife.) Dick had gone in search of a late-night snack and George had dashed off to the room she's sharing here with Anne to commit her day's events to her diary.

I had been watching Anne very closely all evening. She seemed unnaturally upset at the thought that someone had deliberately taken our bags and kidnapped old George. Her manner was almost guilty. I know she is a sensitive girl, but even making allowances for that, I thought her behaviour decidedly odd. You see, I had a strong feeling that I knew what was going on.

I gently asked her if she had mentioned anything about the Captain's papers to the reporter during their tea with Aunt Fanny and Uncle Quentin. She assured me that she hadn't said a word about our secret. She said she was so worried about keeping a secret as important as ours, that she purposely didn't talk about it, instead telling the reporter about our plans for a camping holiday in the woods before returning to school on September 1st. I sensed that she hadn't finished, so I stayed silent and didn't press her.

"But," she said then, "I did talk to Miss Butlerton again, after our tea." She couldn't look me in the eye and I felt terribly sorry for her.

"Don't worry, old girl," I said in a comforting way. "Tell me what happened. It could be important."

This is what she told me:

"Miss Butlerton called me yesterday to wish us a happy holiday in the woods. I did think it was jolly sweet of her and . . . well . . . oh! I'm terribly sorry, Julian, but I'm afraid I told her that we'd changed our plans and would be holidaying on the Scilly Isles instead! She was surprised to hear it and asked what had made us decide to do that? I told her we'd become interested in the area after reading about Captain Kirrin's ship and she went very quiet then. After a moment she asked how I knew the ship had gone down off the Scilly Isles, and then I knew I'd done a silly thing! I was awfully stupid, wasn't I?"

I did what I could to comfort Anne. I know that she wasn't acting maliciously and Miss Butlerton had rather befriended her. Anne is a very trusting person.

Still, I am now feeling quite suspicious about that reporter. George said it might have been a woman that was looking through our bags – I wonder if it was Miss Butlerton? I will have to be vigilant about her. I shan't say anything to the others yet. Our search for the Captain's wreck and the Royal Dragon of Siam <u>will</u> continue.

Over a breakfast of fresh bread, home-smoked kippers, fried eggs and a juicy bone for Timmy, all the Five agreed that we were even more determined to find the wreck of the *Peregrine* and search it for the Royal Dragon. We were so fascinated by this heirloom that belonged to the royal family of Siam – we desperately wanted to know what it was. But we still had no idea where in the waters surrounding the Scilly Isles it might be.

Uncle had arranged for us to stay in a guest house on St Agnes, where our search would begin. We were to arrive there on the 22nd, leaving us a day or two to explore Penzance. We still had plenty of time before returning to Kirrin with Uncle on the 29th.

A heavy rain kept us indoors that morning, so we wasted no time in returning to the boys' bedroom and examining the Captain's papers once again. The log had nothing more to tell us, so we began reading through the letters. In no time at all, Dick had made an intriguing discovery. In an envelope containing a letter from the Duke of Dibeltoynn, we found a small note written in the Captain's own hand, and a curious diagram.

What a fool I have been!
The tragic wreck of the Peregrine was no accident. There was a traitor among my crew – a wrecker! He must have been working with someone and it was they who gave me a guide light straight on to those jagged rocks. The Peregrine's hull was torn out instantly. I am certain I know the vile traitor. No doubt he escaped before my ship sank. The treasure is lost at sea. What a vicious plot! This murderous villain must be brought to justice. Not only has he caused the death of many good, honest men, he is in danger of causing a civil war in Siam! I will write separately to inform the Duke of the rogue's identity. It is of the utmost importance and nobody else must know.

H.J.K
October 26th, 1859

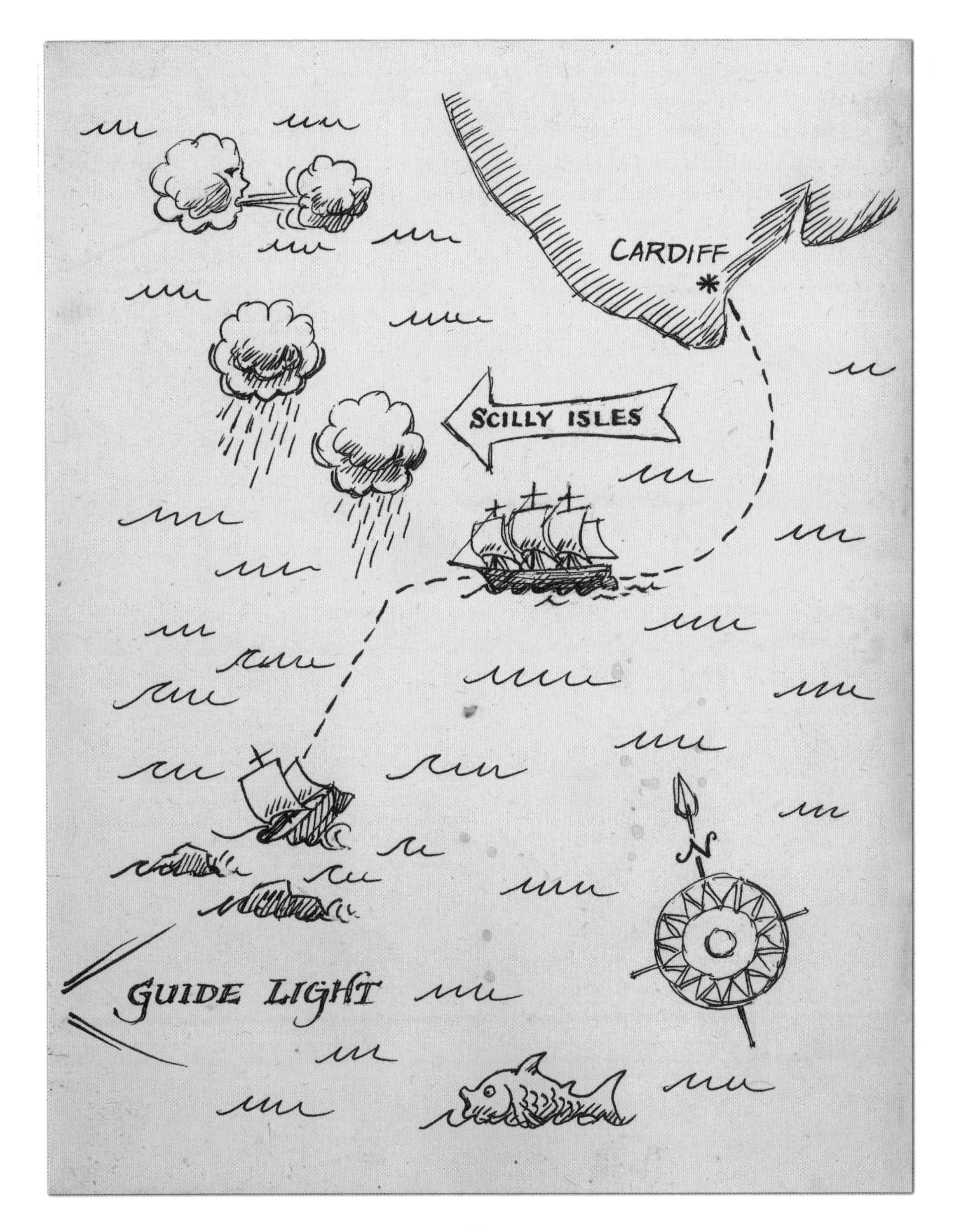
CARDIFF
SCILLY ISLES
GUIDE LIGHT
N

The Captain had been betrayed by a crew member! The dishonourable sailor had purposely guided the ship on to rocks and certain wreckage. How fiendish!

The Captain's use of the word 'treasure' thrilled us all. Here was the first bit of proof we'd found that the legend Miss Butlerton had spoken of was true – the *Peregrine* had indeed been carrying a valuable treasure! And it must have sunk along with the Captain's ship, just as we had thought!

We turned immediately to the pile of the Duke's letters, hoping to find another clue to this mesmerizing mystery.

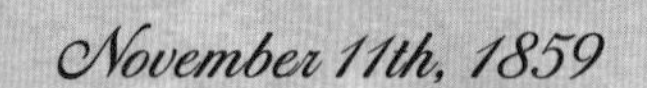

November 11th, 1859

Dear Captain H. J. Kirrin,

What you told me in your last letter, dear Sir, is horrifying! It is unimaginable that a member of your own crew could be responsible for such a dastardly deed. To think, you trusted this man as one of your officers! It is a sad reminder that evil can sometimes wear an impenetrable mask. This villain gave no thought to the many lives of good men that were squandered for his own ill-gotten gains. A man such as this must be found and brought to justice at once. I will use every means in my power to help you do this.

Your friend,

W. Courtenhay

The Duke of Dibeltoynn

HVMW NV Z NZK GL DSVIV GSV HSRK HZMP

This was the only letter that referred to Captain Kirrin's discovery. But it didn't tell us what happened next. We were disappointed that there was no mention of the traitor's name, or how the Captain and his friend were planning to bring him to justice. We even tried to read the letter through the Duke's code-reader, but it revealed nothing.

Suddenly, Anne snatched up the letter and studied it for a long time with a quizzical look on her face. She had noticed the series of random letters at the bottom of the page and was sure it was a secret message. She immediately set about cracking the Duke's new code.

Anne spotted that V was the most common letter used in the message and substituted it with E. After a lot of concentration and some scratching out and starting again, Anne had decoded the secret message: SEND ME A MAP TO WHERE THE SHIP SANK. She was simply super!

Anne had discovered a new clue in the mystery of the Royal Dragon. After seeing the decoded message, we all agreed that the Captain must have sent the Duke a secret map to where the *Peregrine* went down. That's where the treasure would be. We had to find that secret map!

D.K. 21st August, 1959

I've left the others upstairs discussing our latest discovery about Captain Kirrin, the Peregrine, and the Royal Dragon. I wanted some time alone to think. I feel sure we are missing something.

I'm in Mr Pollack's library (he's the scientist friend of Uncle's that we're staying with here). Mr Pollack seems to have even more dusty old books than Uncle Quentin! I must say, though, that Mrs Pollack is a fine cook. I can tell that we shall eat like kings while we are here. Last night, we enjoyed such a feast that even I couldn't clear my plate!

Dick old boy, you must focus your mind!

Right. Let's see ...

On learning that a traitor had deliberately wrecked the Peregrine, the Duke asked our great-great-great-grandfather to send him a map of where the clipper went down. That must mean they planned to find the treasure and make another attempt to return it to Siam before a civil war ensued.

The others are all discussing how we'll go about finding the treasure map. But I don't see how we can! It's a horrible thought, but when Ju and I took those papers from the Captain's box, we may have left the most important clue behind. That would have to mean that reporter Butlerton has the treasure map! On the other hand, if the Captain sent the map to the Duke, then it wouldn't have been inside his box. It would have to be with the Duke ... in which case, I don't see how we'll ever lay our hands on it. Blow!

I'll see if the others fancy a walk to the village. I spotted a rather wonderful-looking baker's on our way through yesterday. I'm starving!

That lunchtime, we sat inside the baker's shop and ate fresh bread with honey, ham and egg pies, jam tarts and cream cakes, all washed down with homemade ginger beer. Dick had shared his thoughts with us and we were all very impressed with his "powers of deduction" (that was the phrase that Julian used, much to Dick's delight). We had to admit he was right. If we couldn't discover where the *Peregrine* had gone down, we'd never be able to search the wreck for the Royal Dragon. We all felt rather flat.

The baker's wife ran the little shop and, having no other customers to talk to, struck up a conversation with us. (She was a rather talkative woman.)

"You kids shouldn't be lazing about in here just because it's raining outside. You should be doing something educational. There's lots to do around here. Go and look around the castle, why don't you? Learn about our history."

Now, we Five loved visiting old castles when we were children. With nothing else to do and frustrated by our fruitless search for the Captain's map, we all agreed that a visit to the local castle was a very good idea. What we heard next made Anne gasp and George leap from her chair, knocking it over.

"It's quite a place, Dibeltoynn Castle. The Duke himself used to live there a hundred or so years ago. My nephew, John, is the head gardener and, my, those gardens are just lovely. He keeps them wonderfully neat. Tell him I sent you and he'll show you around."

The Duke of Dibeltoynn's Castle! Minutes from where we were standing. What a piece of luck! We hurriedly asked the good lady for directions and set off for the castle at once. Surely, there could be no better place in which to search for clues about the Captain's map!

Chapter Four

Castle Clues

We excitedly made our way to the castle. John the gardener was easy to spot, with his wellingtons and wheelbarrow of compost. We told him his aunt had recommended him to us and he kindly offered to look after Timmy while we children explored the castle. Timmy was a little disgruntled until John introduced him to a lively fox-terrier named Bobs. Then he seemed to like the arrangements. He gave a smart bark, as if to say "I'd much rather be out here with Bobs than in that musty old castle." We left the two dogs to John; no doubt they would get under his feet, but the gardener didn't seem to mind.

Dibeltoynn Castle was terribly grand. We joined a guided tour to learn more about it, hanging at the back of the small group in case we wanted to slip away. We learned that this imposing fortress had been built in the 13th Century, making it over 600 years old. It had always been the 'seat' of the nobles of Dibeltoynn and had undergone significant reconstruction in the mid-1800s, when the then Duke took great pains to restore the original structures and underground passages. We children got very excited at that!

The guide showed us a large plan of the buildings (we've included a copy here), explaining that although it was marked with the several secret passages and hidden rooms that had already been found, there were rumours that there were still more to be discovered. The guide smiled at the group, and a few of the tourists sniggered.

We Five were accustomed to grown-ups dismissing talk of underground passages and secret rooms in this way. It made for an interesting story but was something the grown-ups were completely unwilling to take seriously. (In fact, we were often treated this way ourselves and, we must say, we took great delight in proving the grown-ups wrong!)

Study the Castle plans and then turn to George's diary entry for that day. As you'll see, she uncovered something very interesting inside the Duke's castle ...

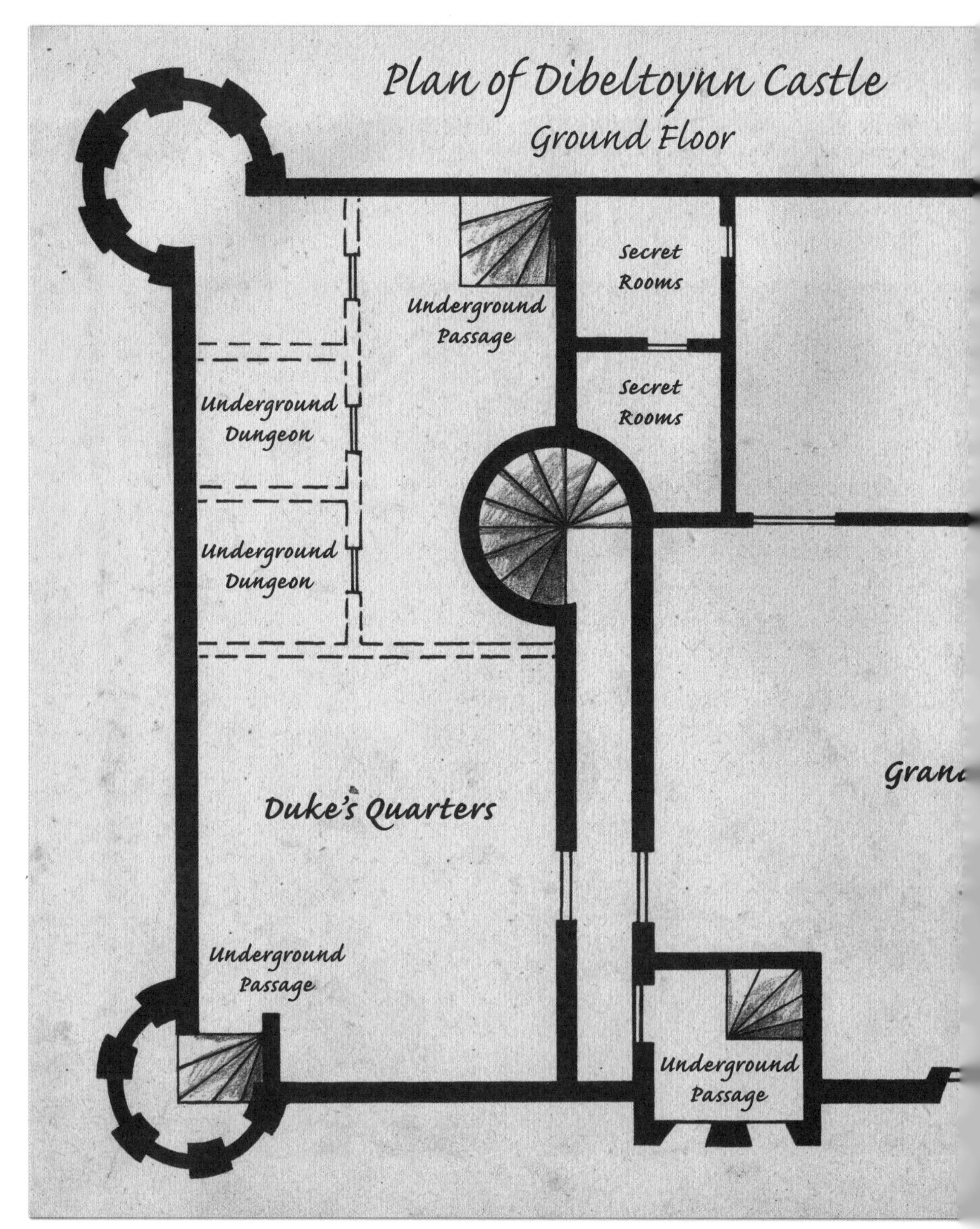
Plan of Dibeltoynn Castle
Ground Floor
Secret Rooms
Underground Passage
Secret Rooms
Underground Dungeon
Underground Dungeon
Duke's Quarters
Underground Passage
Underground Passage

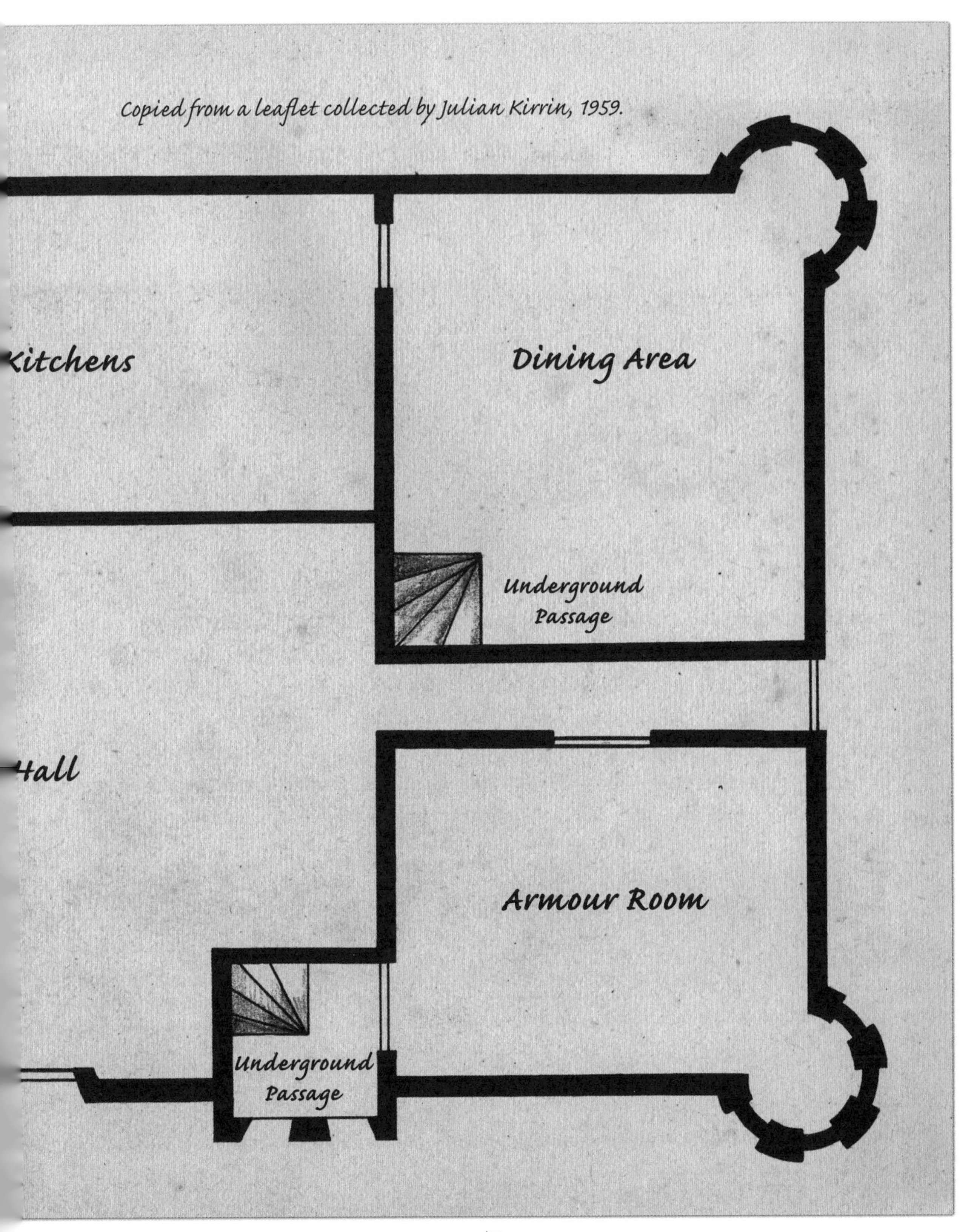
Copied from a leaflet collected by Julian Kirrin, 1959.
Kitchens
Dining Area
Underground Passage
Hall
Armour Room
Underground Passage

From the desk of Georgina Kirrin

(In the heading "Georgina" is crossed out to read "George".)

August 21st, 1959
Dibeltoynn Castle

I was almost enjoying myself in the grand old castle (it would have been much better if Timmy had been with us but the stuffy old guards wouldn't let him come inside). I was a little distracted until the guide mentioned underground passages. At that, my ears immediately pricked up and I turned my full attention to that large old plan showing all the buildings of the castle. My, it is enormous.

Next we visited the Armour Room and you simply won't believe what I found! In the corner was an old suit of armour (16th Century, Julian said – he'd been studying the leaflet of course!) that looked different to the others. It wasn't as shiny or looked-after. Well, I know that if I wanted one suit of armour to attract less attention than others, I'd certainly put it in a corner and let it become dull and dirty. So naturally that was the suit that I had to take a closer look at ...

There was the Duke of Dibeltoynn's coat of arms on its breast, just like the others. But this suit was also marked with another, far more interesting emblem. On the left arm, close to the wrist was a small engraving of a dragon. The other arm held a sword, but I couldn't take my eyes off the dragon. I must have stared at it for a long time because I suddenly became aware of Julian behind me, telling me everyone had moved on to another room and to hurry up.

"Go and get the others," I told him. Well, he must have sensed from my voice that I'd found something, because he rushed off to get Dick and Anne straightaway.

When we were all together and sure that nobody else was about, I pointed to the engraving of the dragon. Anne gasped and Dick 'oohed'. "Lift up the arm, George," said Julian, so I did. And, oh my goodness! A large section of wall directly behind the suit of armour simply slid aside, revealing solid darkness behind! I had found a secret passage!

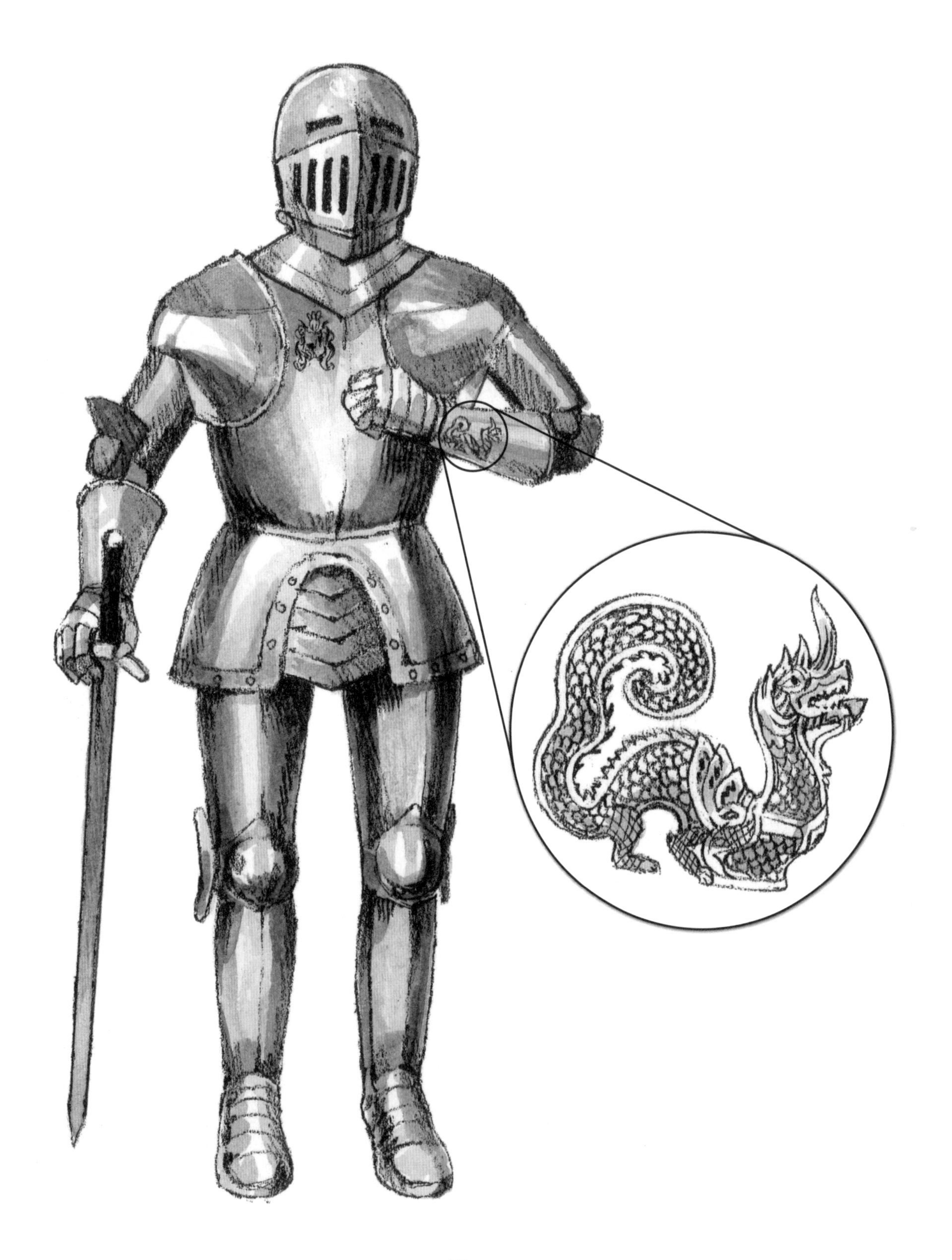

OPEN SESAME!

By Fred Trotteville

How to find secret passages and hidden rooms

As a semi-professional investigator and sometime sleuth, I have acquired a sixth sense for secret passages. Here, I answer the questions that I'm frequently asked about locating hidden tunnels and rooms.

WHICH BUILDINGS HAVE SECRET PASSAGES?

- Castles.
- Stately homes.
- Tombs.
- Stables.
- Extraordinary buildings (say the home of an international arms dealer, criminal boss or old adventurer) may indeed have a few hidden ways in and out of the structure!

WHERE TO LOOK?

- Fireplaces.
- Bookshelves.
- Closet walls.
- Libraries.
- Disused rooms.

The thrill of finding a hidden door, a trick panel, or a secret staircase is like no other! Happy hunting! Fred

HOW DO YOU MAKE YOUR WAY INSIDE?

- Tap the walls and floors and listen for a hollow sound.
- A suspiciously hollow echo behind the wall means there may be a secret passage there.
- Tug large books on the bookshelf, or look for a loose stone in the fireplace. Anything may be a trigger device that will cause a wall to slide open or a bookshelf to turn like a wheel.
- Intricate panelling often harbours a hidden passage. Press on the corners of the panels, try pushing and sliding them in various directions.
- Feel around under the edges of desks, there may be a secret button hidden there.
- Look for odd decorations such as suits of armour, large statues, or ornate wooden carvings. Often latches are hidden among these deceptive pieces.
- Look for disturbances in the dust: if there are any, this may be a clue that someone has done something there recently.
- Run your fingers around the edges of cabinets and fireplaces.
- Don't forget the floor! Roll back rugs and look for large metal rings or irregular flooring that may conceal a trap door.

By lifting the arm on the suit of armour, George triggered a device in the stone wall. It caused a large block of stone to slide away and created an opening just large enough for us to squeeze past the suit and crawl through. We quickly entered the passageway and slid the stone nearly closed behind us. (In situations like these, it's important to remain hidden at the same time as leaving oneself an escape route.)

Julian went first, then the girls, and Dick last. The boys lit our path with their torches and we slowly made our way down a narrow tunnel. The tunnel was very low in places so that we had to crouch down and crawl along the hard-packed dirt floor. It was obvious that the passage hadn't been used in years. Julian cleared the cobwebs from the path but many sticky webs still brushed across our faces and arms. Poor Anne; she shivered with disgust at the eerie sensation.

Finally we came to a thick wooden door. Julian tugged and pushed on its handle until the door flew open, toppling Julian to the ground. He jumped to his feet and we carefully stepped into the hidden room. It was small and perfectly round. The boys flashed their torches along the walls. There was a grand ring of columns around the outside but otherwise the room was empty. We could see no windows or stairs, or contents of any kind. Julian and Dick turned their torches to the floor and we all gasped. In the middle of the room was a striking yellow, orange and red sunburst inlaid into the stone floor. The sun's rays were formed of coloured stone cut into narrow panels and artfully arranged.

We all fell to our knees and ran our fingers along each ray of the sunburst, hoping to find a loose panel or reveal some other clue. But there was nothing to be found. Julian suggested we run our fingers along the walls so we jumped up, eager to continue our hunt. All except Anne, who was tired and had had quite enough of the dreary and dark underground. Noticing her discomfort, Julian asked her to find a nice spot in the gardens outside, where we would join her shortly for a well-earned snack (we had brought extra food with us from the baker's shop). Taking Dick's torch, Anne set off, promising to find Timmy so that he could join us again.

The rest of us stayed and searched every inch of that hidden room, especially the sunburst on the floor. Then we realized that we were all quite starved and reluctantly left off searching to join Anne for our well-deserved feast.

Anne's Diary - 21st August, 1959

Dibeltoynn Castle, the formal gardens

Dear Diary,

After the rain earlier, I am so pleased to see that the sun is shining and the clouds have lifted outside. I did feel terribly stuffy and cooped up struggling along that musty secret passage. And that dark little room! Oh, it made me feel like the walls were closing in on us. I was grateful to Julian for suggesting I get our picnic ready, though I didn't much like having to crawl through that dusty tunnel by myself.
I found Timmy and Bobs playing together, not far from where gardener John was trimming some tall and fine green hedges. John directed me to these formal gardens, which are simply marvellous! I've had a jolly walk and am now waiting for the others to join me for a delicious picnic. John's aunt from the baker's shop has given us four cheese sandwiches, four of ham-and-mustard, some tomatoes, a whole chocolate cake and two flasks of lemonade. It does look far too much for just the five of us but I dare say that with Dick and Timmy around, we'll manage to get through it all right!

I've found us a wonderful spot inside 'The Compass Garden'. It's fairly secluded and set out so cleverly. Inside a large, round bed, are planted scores of roses in eight spokes, each one representing a different point on the compass. Surrounding the roses are lots of pale pebbles, giving the effect of a glorious red-and-white star set against a backdrop of shiny, pinkish grey! Seven of the eight spokes are white, and the final one is red. It's quite dramatic and, I think, awfully clever. John tells me that the castle shop will have a postcard of it so I shall be sure to buy one before we leave.

N

We joined Anne for a truly delicious picnic in the gardens. The day had turned warm and sunny and all about us was the lovely scent of roses. We were full to bursting and sat in comfortable silence, enjoying the feeling of being outdoors, just us Five together.

We agreed with Anne that the castle's gardens were wonderfully set out and that John must be a gifted gardener to keep them looking so fine. Julian got out his compass to check that the roses were correctly set out and declared their directions faultless.

Quite suddenly, something came over Dick! He sprang up in great excitement and cried, "Hurry! We've got to get back to the secret room!" We all stared at him in shock, especially Anne who didn't want to believe that her brother could really want her to go back through the dank tunnel and into that chilly room she so disliked. But there was Dick, hurriedly packing away our picnic things and telling us we had to search the sunburst again – he thought he knew exactly where to look for the map!

"Buck up, Anne," said Julian. "Let's help Dick with these things. George, you take Timmy back to the gardener and meet us in the room, as quickly as you can!"

When George joined us in the secret room, Dick was kneeling on the floor, examining the sunrays by the light of Julian's torch. "The red roses in the compass garden were a clue! There's something hidden in the floor under one of these sun rays. I just know it!" said Dick.

He pried at several of the inlaid stones but none of them would come loose. He wasn't able to slip his knife blade into a single crack.

"Julian, which way is northwest?" asked Dick. "That's the direction the red roses highlighted. We just need to find northwest and then we'll know which sunray to look under!"

HOW TO READ A COMPASS

Find your way, night or day

A compass is probably the most important piece of equipment a traveller can have. It's all very well and good having a nice shiny compass complete with spinning needle that will keep you fascinated for hours, but just how do you use one properly?

COMPASS BASICS

• A compass is a tool to help you work out which direction you are facing. It has four main points - north, south, east and west. If you think of a compass as a clock face, north is at 12, east is at 3, south is at 6 and west is at 9.

• It has a moving needle, which can move around in a circle like a clock hand. Unlike a clock hand, it can move in both directions.

• The moving needle will always point to the north. The end that is pointing to the north may be shaped like an arrow, or coloured red.

• Keep the compass level or the needle will not move freely.

• Make sure the compass is kept away from any metallic objects. Knives, torches and even keys can affect the needle.

FIND YOUR WAY

A compass can be quite confusing for a new user, so here are a few basic instructions to get you going.

01. Let's say that you wish to head east from your current position. First, hold the compass level in your hand.

02. Next, note the direction of the painted end of your compass needle. Remember that the needle will always point north (even when it's not pointing at north on your compass).

03. Now, rotate yourself (or rotate your compass if it has an outer bezel) until the painted end of the needle is pointing to the north marker on your compass.

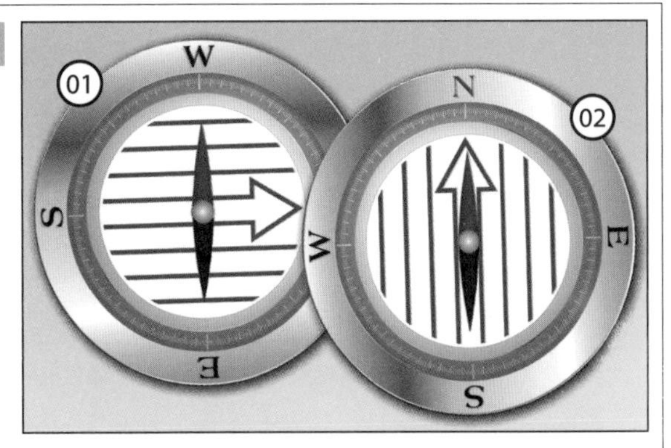

04. A simple reading from your compass will now give you the direction of north, south, east or west, so you can turn to the east and keep going.

MAPS AND COMPASSES

01. Locate your position on the map by paying attention to local landmarks and terrain.

02. Place the edge of the compass on the map so it is next to your current position.

03. If you are using an orienteering compass, adjust the compass so the edge forms a straight line from your current position to your desired destination. If using a standard compass make sure the direction arrow painted on the compass is directed at your desired destination.

04. Keeping the compass steady on the map turn the bezel so the orienting lines (the lines painted on the face of the compass) line up with the meridian lines on your map. Make sure you have your map the right way round with north at the top.

05. With the compass still on the map look along your direction arrow on the compass which should still be pointing towards your destination. Take a reading from the markings on the edge of the compass to show which direction your destination is.

06. Holding the compass flat in your hand follow the compass along the heading you took from the markings on the edge of the compass.

D.K. 21st August, 1959
Pollacks' thatched cottage

Our trip to Dibeltoynn Castle today was full of excitement! Not only did old George discover a secret room but we also uncovered some more clues. We found an old leather envelope full of the captain's letters to the Duke, but no map. What a disappointment! But thrilling, all the same.

It was me who worked out the puzzle! Anne's little compass rose garden was the key! You see, those red roses gave me the clue we needed. Back in the secret room, all I had to do was find northwest on the compass in order to reveal the Duke's hiding place.

I worked out the correct sunray and didn't even have to pry it with my knife blade. I just pressed on one side of the stone inlay and the whole ray lifted up like it was on a hinge! Underneath was a small golden box and inside the box was the envelope with the Captain's papers! (Or are they the Duke's papers since the Captain sent them to him?)

Anyway, a quick look through them was enough to show that the Duke's papers didn't contain the map we are after, which is a blow. The box is here with us now and we shall examine the papers properly after dinner. I wonder what they have to say? What an adventure! And I worked it all out on my own. Hurrah! I feel certain that we Five will solve the mystery of the Royal Dragon very quickly!

Mrs Pollack is calling us for dinner. I say, I must write again later for we fell upon another surprise as we left Dibeltoynn Castle. Would you believe that we ran into that reporter woman?

We were amazed to have found the Duke's papers. No map but we did find several letters from Captain Kirrin to the Duke and we were certain they would contain many more clues about what had happened to the Siamese treasure.

Our excitement continued all through dinner. Back at the old cottage, Mrs Pollack had prepared a roast chicken, sweet carrots, and lots of warm, fresh bread with homemade butter. A giant apple pie and fresh, thick cream finished off our feast. Even Uncle Quentin looked delighted!

While we all helped ourselves to second servings, Julian remarked how wonderful it was in the gardens and how nice it would be to enjoy the outdoors for a while. He wondered what we would say to camping in the nearby woods for a night before we headed off to St Agnes and the Scilly Isles. Mr Pollack immediately agreed that the woods of Penzance were perfect for camping and encouraged Uncle to let us go. Thankfully, Uncle Quentin thought our idea excellent.

It was decided. The Five would set off the next morning and camp overnight, delaying our arrival in St Agnes until the 24th. Julian told us later that he'd cleverly planned this excursion so that we could examine the Duke's papers away from any prying eyes. If you're going to be a good adventurer, it helps to be as clever as Julian. (Of course, if he had known the troubles that were to befall us in the woods, and that our trip to St Agnes would be delayed by five days instead of two, he might never have made this suggestion.)

The Diary of Julian Kirrin - Penzance

21st August, afternoon

I had a terrible surprise when we left the Castle this afternoon. We ran straight into reporter Butlerton! She's here in Penzance. She looked just as surprised to see us, as we her. Then she smiled widely and approached us.

"Why, Anne," she said. "What a lovely coincidence."

Timmy growled and George scowled at her, ready to make some rude remark. I quickly interceded. "Good day, Miss Butlerton. What brings you to Penzance?"

I watched the reporter very carefully. To my mind she seemed decidedly shifty. She ignored my question and cunningly asked one of her own.

"Did you children find anything interesting inside the castle?"

I told her it was a fascinating place and well worth a visit. Then I brought the conversation to an end by claiming that we were late in meeting Uncle Quentin.

I don't believe that her question was an innocent one and I think we'll do well to alter our plans a little and spend some time in the woods. Butlerton knows that we plan to visit the Scilly Isles and I want to have a good look at the Duke's papers before we get there.

Our camping gear is already packed and we're to set out early tomorrow. I wouldn't put it past that reporter to follow us.

What a peculiar woman! I dare say she means us no good.

Chapter Five

Into the Woods

Early the next morning, we borrowed a map from Mr Pollack and headed to a path he'd marked that would take us into the lush green woods. He'd suggested we camp in a clearing surrounded by magnificent old trees near to a gurgling brook. We could hardly wait to stretch our legs on a nice wooded path.

This next part of our story is full of notes on camping and the outdoors. (If you're impatient to learn more about the Mystery of the Royal Dragon, you should turn straight to page 110 – but remember to come back and study our Guide to Perfect Camping.)

There was, and still is, nothing the Famous Five like better than camping out in the wild. It's exhilarating! But it can quickly turn into a nightmare if you don't know what you're doing. The key to a successful camping trip is preparation. Be sure to study the information in this chapter carefully – it will prepare you for your own thrilling adventures in the great outdoors.

We made our way along the trail, talking excitedly and all at once. We were each sharing our own ideas about what makes a place ideal for camping; even Timmy joined in with a loud bark that we knew meant the spot "should have plenty of rabbits"!

We stopped to watch the butterflies and squirrels, and to enjoy the fine array of wildflowers all around – there is always so much to see in the countryside, no matter the season. We might have gone on all day like this but Julian finally said that if we didn't hurry, we'd be arriving at our campsite in the dark.

Julian always planned our camping trips. Here, we've included his notes on what to take and how to set up camp for maximum enjoyment and efficiency. We have relied on his notes for years and can't better them.

THE FAMOUS FIVE GUIDE TO PERFECT CAMPING

THINGS TO REMEMBER

1. Always plan to arrive at your camping destination in the DAYTIME. You want to avoid putting up your tent in the dark or it could turn into quite a muddle!

2. Plan your route carefully so that you know where you're going and roughly how long it will take you to get there. I always make sure our trips are based on how far Anne can walk in a day. (Anne is the youngest and slowest of us, so we set our pace to hers, which is the fair and proper thing to do.)

3. Always have in mind a Plan B - if you ever feel tired out along your route, you'll be able to select other places to camp.

4. If you're camping in a group, it's a good idea to agree before you set off on what makes a great campsite. You don't want to be arguing over whether your camp should have sun or shade, or be at the top or bottom of a mountain. If your spot matches the list, you won't argue.

5. Make sure you are well equipped! Be sure to take enough food and supplies to last for the duration of your trip. I have a checklist of what is to be packed in each of our bags, with myself carrying the heaviest things and Anne the lightest.

CAMP MUST HAVES

- A sunny clearing.
- Flat ground with no stones, sticks, or holes.
- Out of the wind or has bushes that can block the wind - most wind comes from the west so set up your tent facing south or east.
- Near a fast moving river or stream, but not too close.
- Collect water at least 30 feet upstream from your camp to be sure it isn't contaminated!

NICE EXTRAS

- Swimming hole - One that's also good for fishing is ideal.
- Plenty of firewood
- Fruit trees - These provide tasty and convenient snacks.

MUST AVOID!

- Dry stream or river beds - If there's heavy rain these flood in a flash and quickly turn back into rivers.
- Still water - mosquitoes live in stagnant water.
- Dense woods - not enough sunlight. You'll get cold, wet and buggy at night.
- Tall trees that can attract lightning.
- Dead trees - These could fall on you in a strong wind.
- Ants, bees, or wasps - You don't want to share your campsite with these little beasts!
- Snakes!

THINGS TO PACK

Because there were four of us travelling together (five with Timmy, of course!) we were able to split the load between us! Sharing the heavy objects between the members of the group is the best way of making sure everyone's pack is manageable.

George's Pack

- ☑ Torch
- ☑ Spare clothes
- ☑ Towel
- ☑ Towel for Timmy
- ☑ Toothbrush
- ☑ 2 water bottles (1 for Timmy)
- ☑ Whistle
- ☑ Sleeping bag
- ☑ Blanket for Timmy
- ☑ First Aid Kit
- ☑ Water purification tablets
- ☑ Insect Repellent
- ☑ Timmy's brush
- ☑ Dog bowl
- ☑ Timmy's favourite biscuit treats

To see everything to put in our First Aid kit, see Page 44.

Dick's Pack

- ☑ Head torch
- ☑ Spare clothes
- ☑ Towel
- ☑ Toothbrush
- ☑ Whistle
- ☑ Water bottle
- ☑ Sleeping bag
- ☑ Fishing kit
- ☑ Swiss Army Knife
- ☑ Radio
- ☑ Spare Batteries
- ☑ Flares
- ☑ Binoculars
- ☑ Ropes
- ☑ Small shovel

Dick was always the one to have the latest gadget in his pack. Today he'd pack a GPS and a satellite phone!

Anne's Pack

- ☑ Torch
- ☑ Spare clothes
- ☑ Towel
- ☑ Toothbrush
- ☑ Whistle
- ☑ Water bottle
- ☑ Guide to British wildlife
- ☑ Guide book for identifying wild food
- ☑ Fuel for camping stove
- ☑ Camping pan
- ☑ Soap
- ☑ Can opener
- ☑ Bottle opener
- ☑ Bags to pack our rubbish in
- ☑ Eating utensils
- ☑ Toilet paper
- ☑ Tea bags
- ☑ Dehydrated food
- ☑ Rice
- ☑ Ginger beer

Our domestic expert, Anne, packed all the food and cooking equipment.

Julian's Pack

- ☑ Torch
- ☑ Spare clothes
- ☑ Towel
- ☑ Toothbrush
- ☑ Whistle
- ☑ Water bottle
- ☑ Sketch book
- ☑ Journal
- ☑ Pens
- ☑ Tent
- ☑ Tarpaulin
- ☑ Ground mat
- ☑ Sleeping Bag
- ☑ Adventure books to read
- ☑ Maps
- ☑ Compass
- ☑ Matches or flint
- ☑ Anne's sleeping bag
- ☑ Anne's Camping Stove

Being the strongest I also helped carry some of Anne's equipment.

CAMP SET-UP AND LAYOUT

Get your tents in a row

Setting out on your first camping trip can be a daunting task. Even a trip to the local woods for a few days can seem like climbing Everest for those who have never done it before. Follow our simple tips and you'll soon find yourself camping like a pro.

THE BASICS

01. Set up your campsite within easy reach of water. Don't get too near, though, as you don't want your campsite to be washed away in a flash flood.

02. Choose level ground for your campsite. You don't want to be rolling out of your tent all night, or trying to balance things on your campfire because you are on a slope!

03. Check for trampled vegetation or broken tree limbs or bushes. Don't place yourself in the centre of an animal's trail to their water source or you never know what unwanted visitors you may get during the night.

PITCH YOUR TENT

01. Make sure you clear the area where you pitch your tent. A lumpy ground sheet is not comfortable!

02. Never pitch your tent under a tree. The rain will keep you awake at night and under a tree you are a major target for lightning strikes.

03. Don't pitch your tent with the opening facing into the wind. Your tent will be cold and draughty and could well blow away.

04. Tents and sleeping bags should be arranged around your campfire, but a good distance away from the flames!

SET UP YOUR CAMPFIRE

01. Keep your fire away from tents and vegetation that may catch light from stray embers.

02. Never leave a campfire unattended and make sure you put it out before you go to sleep - never leave a fire burning overnight!

03. Take the wind direction into account. A tent full of smoke is not fun.

04. Only use dead wood you find on the ground. Never break limbs off trees.

HINTS AND TIPS

01. Take anything you don't want to get wet into your tent at night. Having to put on clothes soaked in dew is very uncomfortable.

02. Hang your food from a branch in a well-sealed container or bag so that scavengers can't get it at night.

03. Designate a place to be your camp toilet area. It is best to choose a secluded spot that is fairly close, but separated from your campsite by trees or large shrubs. Make sure all waste is buried.

04. 'Leave no trace'. Make sure you leave your campsite the way you found it. This includes:
    - Take all rubbish with you.
    - Extinguish your fire properly.
    - Make sure all human waste is well buried or properly disposed of.
    - Do not throw anything into the water, this includes rubbish, dirty washing water, human waste and food scraps.

We walked for a little over an hour and reached a place in the forest where the trees grew wide and tall and a nearby stream flowed fast and cold.

Julian located the river on his map. "The clearing is over the hill on the other side of the river. We'll set our tents there," he said.

We headed up a gentle slope and found a fairly large circular clearing of soft grass. There were clumps of brush that blocked any wind that might blow. We wanted to stay out of the wind or we'd be chilled through by morning. The clearing had everything we liked best about a campsite. There was plenty of firewood, a river and some blackberry bushes nearby.

Julian had us get to work right away to set up camp. It helps to have someone take charge and allocate the key tasks – otherwise, everyone will decide to collect firewood and the tents won't go up. Julian and George put up the tents with Anne's help. Dick set about collecting a store of firewood and got a cheerful fire burning. Then, while George fetched water, Anne set up our camp kitchen. Timmy liked to help us with the ropes and firewood – it's a great idea to have a strong and clever dog with you when you go camping.

THE FAMOUS FIVE GUIDE TO PERFECT CAMPING

FOUR STEPS TO CAMP SET-UP
(in order of importance to your survival in the wild)

Step 1 - Shelter
Step 2 - Fire
Step 3 - Water
Step 4 - Food

REMEMBER -
the sooner your campsite is set up, the sooner you can start to enjoy it.

HOW TO MAKE SHELTER

A healthy human can last for weeks without food and days without water, but only a few hours without proper shelter from the wind and rain. It is therefore essential to know how to build a shelter. Survival equipment such as a tarpaulin or blanket can help to build a protective cover, but it is possible to create a shelter using only the things around you.

HUT SHELTER

This is a basic shelter, which you can make with the materials available in the countryside.

01. Find a level, dry patch of land near a forked tree, tree stump or rock.

02. Find a long log, thick branch or uprooted tree. Rest one end on your tree stump or rock so it forms a long triangle, ideally at a 45° angle.

03. Look for as many loose branches as you can find. Lean these along the first branch. Their tops should be against the branch and they should extend at 45° angles out to the sides. Use the stronger, thicker branches nearest the tree stump as these will form the main part of your shelter walls.

04. Leave just one end open as your entrance – covering the majority of the shelter will better protect you from the elements.

05. Add handfuls of leaves to create an insulating layer. Ideally you should have enough leaves and debris to create a 30cm layer of insulation in order to retain warmth.

TARP SHELTER

This is also a very basic shelter which can be built with just a tarpaulin, parachute or plastic sheet and some rope or cord.

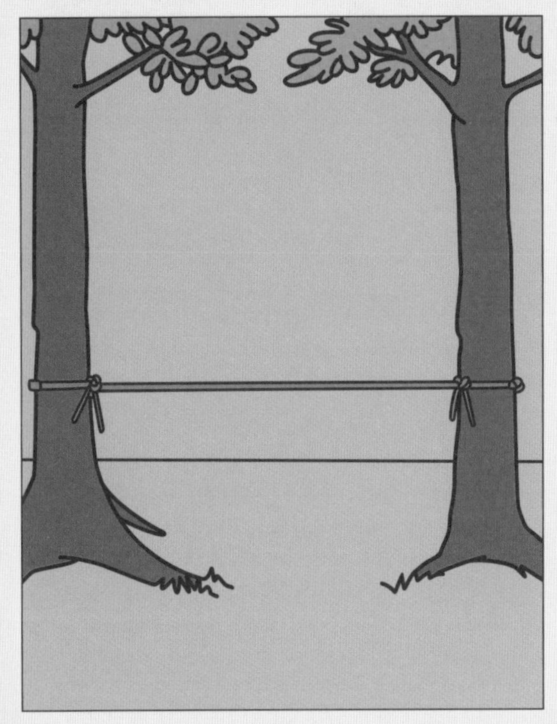

01. Tie your rope between two trees. It should be taut and about 1.5 metres off the ground.

02. Drape your tarp or plastic sheet over the rope, so there are equal amounts of material on each side.

03. Pull the material out to the sides so you have created a basic tent shape.

04. Secure the material in place using large stones or rocks. These work better than stakes as they do not damage your waterproof material.

LOCATION

No matter what sort of shelter you build you need to choose the right location.

01. If you are on high ground, move lower so you will not be as exposed to the weather. If you are in a valley, move to higher ground, warm air rises so the lower ground will tend to be colder and damp.

02. See if you can find any natural resources. Ideally you should be close to a natural water source and fuel, such as dry wood, for your fire.

03. Can you see any animal tracks or trails nearby? You don't want any unwelcome visitors to your camp during the night!

04. Look up. Check there are no loose, dead branches or other debris in the trees above you that could fall if a wind picks up overnight.

HOW TO FIND WATER

You are lost in the wilderness and your bottle or canteen is empty. There's no sign of lakes or rivers nearby and your thirst is growing by the second. What do you do?

ABOVE-GROUND STILL

You will need:

- A sunny slope
- A clear plastic bag
- A small rock with any soil or dirt brushed off
- Leafy green vegetation
- Something to tie the end of the bag
- A piece of tubing, straw, hollow reed if available

01. The most important thing before you start is to make sure none of your vegetation is poisonous or you will have poisoned water.
02. Remove all sticks and anything that may cause a puncture in the bag.
03. Fill the bag with air by holding the edges and facing it into the breeze, or swing it around you until it inflates.
04. Put your green vegetation in the bag until it is around half to three-quarters full.
05. Place the rock in the bag with the greenery.
06. If you have a straw or hollow reed put this into the bag with the end exposed. This will allow you to drain the water without opening the bag.
07. Tie off the end of the bag as tight as possible, if using a tube or straw put a stopper in the end to prevent air escaping from the bag.
08. Place the bag on the sunny slope with the mouth of the bag facing downhill, slightly raised above the rest of the bag, and make sure the bag is fully exposed to the sunlight.
09. The small rock you placed in the bag should be at the lowest point in the bag.
10. To retrieve the water, wait around 24 hours and either use the tube you inserted, or untie the mouth of the bag to release the water that has gathered around the rock.
11. Once you have drained the water, replace the vegetation and repeat the entire process to obtain the maximum water available.

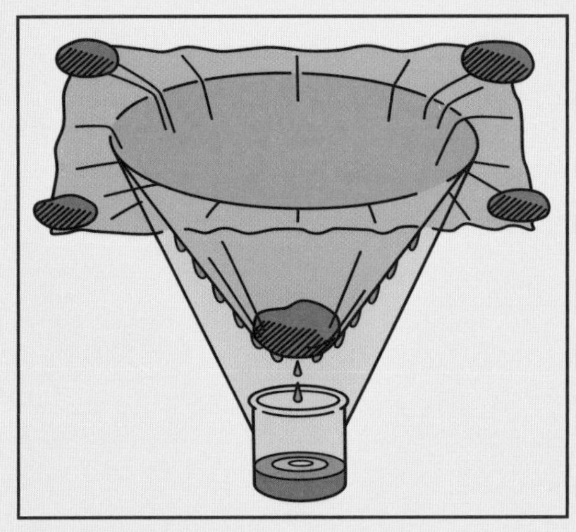

SOLAR STILL

You will need:
- Large plastic sheet or tarpaulin
- Something to collect your water in
- A medium sized rock (around 500g)
- A number of heavier rocks

01. Dig a conical hole in the ground around 1.5 metres wide at the top and narrowing until you reach around 60cm in depth to the bottom.
02. The bottom of the hole should be in the centre with equal distance from each side.
03. Put your collection device at the bottom of the hole, a medium saucepan or pot is best.
04. Lay your plastic sheet or tarpaulin over the hole. Place your larger rocks around the outside of the sheet at the perimeter of your hole and pull the sheet to stop it touching the sides of your hole.
05. Place the medium sized rock in the centre so it is over your pot.
06. The centre of the sheet should have sagged under the weight of the rock to sit around 45 centimetres below the surface of the ground with the rock sitting about 15 centimetres above the pot.
07. Wait 24 hours.
08. Water vapour from the soil and atmosphere will form on the underside of your sheet and drip into the pot below.
09. A hot day and a cold night will give you around 600ml of water.
10. Although the water should be safe to drink, it is best to boil it first just to be on the safe side.
11. Remember to move the still you have made every three days as you will have taken all the water you can from that hole.

PURIFY AND STAY SAFE

Any water you collect while adventuring should be purified. Even if the water looks clear and clean, it can still hide microbes and organisms that could make you very sick. Boiling is the best way to purify your water and will kill all harmful organisms and microbes. Many camping stores also sell water purification tablets that do the same job.

01. If your water is cloudy or muddy allow it to stand in a large pot for at least 12 hours to allow settling of the mud or particles. Then carefully scoop out the water and avoid disturbing what has settled.
02. Begin by pouring your water through a clean pillow-case, a piece of denim or, if you have one, a coffee filter. This will remove any large particles or impurities from the water.
03. Place the water in a clean receptacle, place over your camp fire and bring to the boil.
04. When the water is boiling allow it to continue boiling hard for up to two minutes. Boiling for longer will cause you to lose water in steam and also make the water taste flatter. Remember, the higher you are above sea level the quicker the water will boil.
05. Make sure you do not allow your purified water to come into contact with any item that has contained or been in contact with un-purified water as this will re-contaminate it.
06. Stir the water vigorously to add oxygen back into it.
07. Using two clean un-contaminated receptacles, pour the water between the two several times, this once again adds oxygen.
08. Add a little squash if available or powdered water flavourings (available from many hiking and camping stores).

HOW TO MAKE FIRE

You need a break and although you have shelter, you have no way to get warm or cook your food. It's time to get back to basics and make a fire. But with your matches soaked from a river crossing it will take some ingenuity to get a fire going.

STICK TO BASICS

You will need:

- Tinder
- Firewood
- Strong, slightly flexible stick around 60cm long to make main bow
- String or shoelace
- Piece of wood around 5cm wide x 30cm long
- Straight stick around 30cm long x 1.2cm thick to make drill
- Fist-sized rock, seashell or piece of wood
- Lubrication – lip balm, sunscreen, chap stick
- Small piece of dry wood

01. Find some tinder, this can be pocket lint, dried moss or shredded tree bark.

02. Gather firewood of varying sizes from very small and thin to larger pieces for later use. Try not to use wood from the ground as this will be damp, look for dead branches on trees. If branches on a tree bend but don't snap immediately these are alive and too full of sap to be used, whereas dead ones will snap away easily.

MAKE A FIREBOW

01. To make your bow, take a slightly flexible stick and cut a notch in each end. Tie a string or shoelace between the two notches leaving a small amount of slack to attach your drill.

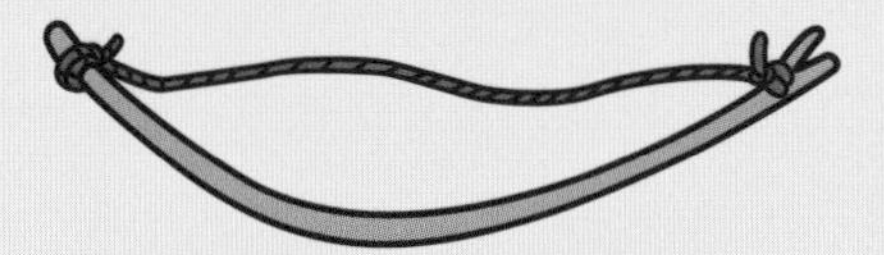

02. Use the straightest piece of wood you can find to make your drill. If you can't find a straight piece you may need to use your knife to whittle one. The straighter the drill, the easier using your firebow will be.

03. Smooth one end of your drill off so it is rounded like the end of a pencil. Now shape the other end into a point, you can use a knife for this or rub it on a rough stone. The sharper the point you have the less friction you will create and the easier it will be to use.

04. Place the drill against your string and loop the string around the drill until the slack is taken up.

FIREBOARDING

01. To make a fireboard use the same type of wood as you used for your drill.

02. Make a mark on the long edge of the board 1.5 times the diameter of your drill in from the edge of the board.

03. Using a knife or stone dig a notch at the mark the same diameter as your drill and about 0.5cm deep.

04. Using your knife cut a 'V' shape in the edge of the wood that reaches from the edge of the wood almost to the centre of the notch you've made.

05. Remember not to cut the notch too big or your drill will slip out.

START YOUR FIRE

01. Place the small piece of wood underneath the board so that your drill tip sits on it. This will be your actual fire starter.

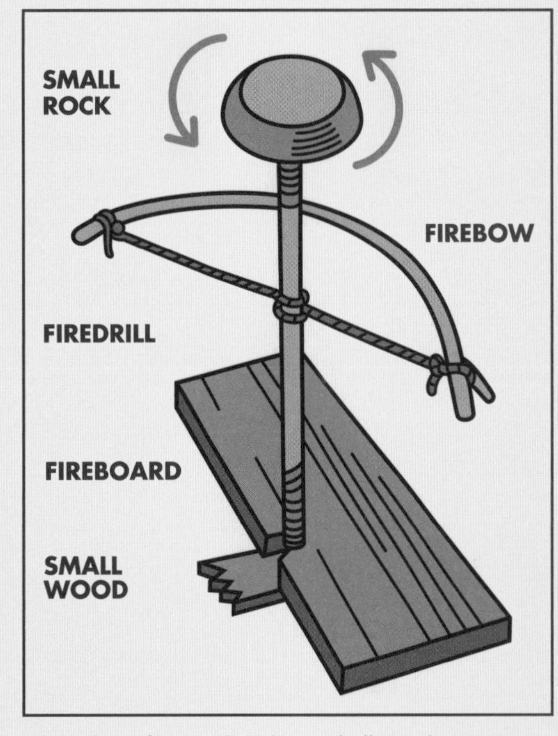

02. Take a fist-sized rock, seashell or whatever you are using, this will be known as your socket. If your socket has a small indentation in it that will comfortably keep the end of your drill in place this will make things easier.

03. Place a little lubrication (lip balm, sunscreen or even ear-wax) in the indentation in the rock.

04. Put the pointed end of your drill, with bow attached, into the socket and the smooth end of your drill into the indent you made in the fireboard.

05. Place your left foot on the fireboard to hold it steady and apply enough pressure on your socket to hold the drill in place.

06. Begin a sawing motion with the bow that will cause the drill to spin.

07. You may need to adjust either the pressure on the socket, or the tension on the line around the drill to achieve a smooth continuous movement.

08. As you begin to get into a rhythm, increase the speed of your sawing and the pressure on the socket.

08. A black powder will begin to form on the fireboard followed by smoke. When you have an increasing amount of smoke coming from the fireboard you are almost there.
09. Gently fan air over the board using your hand, if you must blow on it do it very gently as it is easy to extinguish the ember at this point.
10. As the ember begins to glow, slowly add your tinder a little at a time so as not to smother the ember.
11. Gently blow through the tinder to help the flame spread. Add the smaller sticks from your firewood first and then gradually increase their size until you have your fire.
12. Remember, for safety it is always best to surround your fire with a ring of stones which helps prevent larger pieces of wood from slipping and causing the fire to collapse.

DON'T THROW THAT CAN

You will need:

- Empty drink can
- Chocolate
- Tinder
- Twig
- Sunlight
- Firewood

01. Turn your can over so the concave underside is on top.
02. Take a piece of chocolate and begin polishing the underside of the can by rubbing in circular movements.
03. When the can has a coating of chocolate, use the wrapper or a cloth to continue polishing the can. The chocolate will act as an abrasive, so you may need to re-apply it from time to time.
04. Continue polishing until the base begins to take on a mirror finish. This should take around one hour of polishing.
05. Do not eat the chocolate when you have finished with it as it will contain aluminium from the can.

06. Once you have your can mirrored, take a piece of tinder and hold it over the end of your can. Attaching it to the end of the twig is best to prevent burning your fingers.
07. Adjust the can to catch the light by pointing it directly at the sun. Hold the tinder in the light.
08. To check the positioning of the can and the tinder, move a piece of dark material over the can to see the light beam and its focus.
09. Be careful not to stare at the base of the can for too long.
10. After a short while the tinder should ignite and you can then transfer it to your larger collection of tinder to create your fire.

FIRE FROM WATER

You will need:

- Sunlight
- Cellophane wrap or clear balloon
- Water
- Tinder and firewood

01. Gather the edges of the cellophane together to form a pocket.
02. Fill the pocket with water and tighten the cellophane until it is smooth and makes a lens.
03. Use the lens you have created as you would a magnifying glass and focus the beam of sunlight on your tinder until you get ignition.

MEALS MILES FROM ANYWHERE

Food in the wild needn't be mild

Scratching around and foraging to live off the land is an enjoyable way to get the best out of your trips. But sometimes the end of a hard day on the trail needs something a bit more substantial to help fill a gap and fuel you for the next day. We've consulted with some of the top outdoor chefs to bring you a selection of mouth-watering morsels that should make a nice change from the usual bangers and beans that make up most camping trip menus.

Chilli

Ingredients:
450g Minced beef
1 Large onion chopped
1 to 2 tsp Hot chilli (to taste)
1 tsp Paprika
1 tsp Oregano
1 tsp Cumin
1 Clove garlic
1 tin Chopped tomatoes
1 tin Red kidney beans, drained
1 Red pepper, seeded and diced
1 Green pepper, seeded and diced
Large cooking pan

- Brown the beef in a pan, then remove the meat and set aside leaving the oil behind.
- Add the onion to the pan and cook until softened.
- Drain off excess oil and add the browned beef, paprika, oregano, cumin, garlic and peppers.
- Leave to simmer over coals for half an hour.
- Add kidney beans and simmer for further 20 mins.
- Remove from heat and serve.

Julian, these sound yummy. I'm sure the children would enjoy them! Anne

Sticky Bones

Ingredients:	1 tsp Dry mustard
230ml Vinegar	1 tsp Paprika
115ml Honey	1/4 tsp Black pepper
2 tsp Worcestershire sauce	1 Clove garlic, crushed
115ml Tomato ketchup	1.8kg Beef or Pork ribs
1 tsp Salt	Saucepan
	Baking pan

- Place Worcestershire sauce, vinegar, honey, ketchup, salt, mustard, paprika, pepper, and garlic in saucepan.
- Cover, place over fire and bring to the boil.
- Reduce heat and simmer for 15 mins.
- Place ribs in baking pan and cover with sauce. Leave covered and in a cool place to marinate for at least an hour or longer if possible.
- Place over fire, turning regularly and basting with sauce for 20 minutes or until meat is cooked.
- Remove from fire and serve.

Chicken & Vegetables

Ingredients:	Butter
Half a chicken (boneless/skinless portions or breasts work best)	Garlic
2 Carrots	Salt & Pepper
1 Potato	Herbs (optional, although a pinch of thyme is highly recommended)
1 Medium Onion	Baking foil

- Take some heavy-duty foil and place the chicken in the centre.
- Cut the carrots in half and the potato and peeled onion into quarters and spread around the meat.
- Spread three tablespoons of butter onto vegetables.
- Season well adding herbs and garlic.
- Gather the sides of foil together and fold four to five times then repeat with ends to leave a well-sealed foil parcel.
- Place on hot coals for 15 minutes then turn over for another 15 minutes.
- Open the package and check that the chicken is cooked by inserting a fork into the thickest part of the meat and ensuring the juices are running clear.
- When chicken is completely cooked, open packet and serve.

HOW TO FORAGE FOR FOOD IN THE WILD

When you are stuck in the wild with nothing to eat there are two choices: starvation or using your know-how to find some of the vast array of wild food all around you. Your life might depend on your ability to dig around and find food.

Although there are many edible forms of plants, flowers, berries and fungi there are also a number of highly poisonous, even fatal, types of vegetation. Before you start grabbing anything and everything and sticking it in your mouth, make sure you have properly identified it, using a professional field guide and expert help.

HELPFUL HINTS

01. If the area is used for dog-walking obey the general rule of thumb that you do not pick any items below hand height to avoid contamination.
02. Never completely strip an area of wild food no matter how abundant it may be. Leaving at least some behind will allow the plant to continue to thrive for others and also allow the wide range of wild animals that rely on this 'free' food to survive.
03. Avoid wild food from industrialised areas, where there is a risk of chemical contamination.
04. When collecting food try not to pick from the side of the road. If possible move two to three fields in from roads to avoid pollution of food.

FOOD FOR FREE

BILBERRIES

Also known as the European blueberry, these juicy sweet little fruits can be eaten fresh or used for jams and desserts as well as being an excellent accompaniment to chicken and game. Bilberries can be found growing on low, shrubby plants in pine and fir woods on level, semi-shaded areas and heath-land. Avoid the leaves as they can be toxic.

BLACKBERRIES

A long-time staple of the British fruit world, blackberries offer a free way to experience a wonderfully sweet yet tart treat. Blackberries are simple to find by searching any patch of bramble, due to their ability to grow anywhere. Remember the rules and only pick berries above hand height and away from the roadside.

CEPS

If you are in an area of pine, spruce, fir or oak trees keep an eye out for the potent tasting fungus known as ceps, or more commonly porcini. Its nutty taste and creamy texture make it ideal for use with pasta, although it can be used with almost anything! As with all fungi make certain of your identification before eating or cooking. **Check well before you pick it!**

ELDERBERRIES

The fruit of the elder tree has many uses from winemaking to jams and desserts. Never eat the fruit raw as it contains toxic levels of cyanide. Although the cyanide is destroyed through cooking, the same cannot be said for all other green parts of the plant including any unripened fruit.

SORREL

Wild sorrel could easily be mistaken for just another weed but its sour taste is ideal for adding flavour to almost any soup or meal. The leaves are edible, and vary from green to crimson and deep purple depending upon the time of year. Search for sorrel in meadows and large grassy areas.

CHANTERELLE

An orange-yellow fungus with forked gills that run the length of its stem. Once cleaned, Chanterelle can be used as you would any other mushroom, and adds excellent flavour to many dishes. Do not confuse it with the Jack O' Lantern mushroom which has thinner gills that do not reach all the way to the edge. The Jack O' Lantern is bioluminescent, meaning it glows in the dark, not to mention being extremely poisonous.
Check well before you pick it!

MORELS

Morels can be a real find and are much sought after. They can be found on ground that has been subject to a forest fire, as well as near ash, sycamore, oak and apple trees. They grow between March and June. Be aware that their pitted honeycomb appearance is very similar to the poisonous false morel. If you think you may be travelling to an area that contains morels make sure you familiarize yourself with how they look, and also how the poisonous ones look.
Check well before you pick it!

WILD GARLIC

The broad green leaves of wild garlic resemble spinach, and can be found near canals and in damp woodland areas. Its strong garlic smell makes it easily recognizable and an ideal for use in salads, omelettes and soups. Remember to wash the leaves thoroughly to remove any contamination before use.

FORAGING THROUGH THE YEAR

Here are a few of the things you can find during the year to feast upon.

JANUARY
Bittercress
Dandelion leaves

FEBRUARY
Dandelion leaves
Wild chervil
Chickweed
Primroses
Alexanders
Wood sorrel

MARCH
Wild garlic
Garlic mustard
Sea kale
Sea beet
Watercress
Morels
Lime leaves

APRIL
Nettles
Hogweed shoots
Hop shoots
Dandelions
Chickweed
Hawthorn leaves

MAY
Elderflower
Wild fennel
Sea lettuce

JUNE
Lime flowers
Samphire
Sea purslane
Sea beet
Sea lettuce

JULY
Samphire
Green walnuts
Camomile
Blackberries
Ceps
Chanterelles

AUGUST
Samphire
Blackberries
Wild cherries
Camomile
Apples
Sorrel

SEPTEMBER
Nettles
Rowanberries
Elderberries

OCTOBER
Apples
Rowanberries
Chequerberries
Sloes
Chestnuts
Walnuts
Mushrooms

NOVEMBER
Chestnuts
Mushrooms
Pine needles

DECEMBER
Pine needles
Sea beet
Sea purslane
Mushrooms

With our woodland camp set up to perfection, and a hearty lunch of leftover chicken, potatoes and half a fruit loaf inside us, we finally settled down to the real reason we'd taken our camping trip – searching for more clues about the mystery of the Royal Dragon.

Dick brought out the small box he'd found in Dibeltoynn Castle, and we began to look through the letters that our great-great-great-grandfather had sent to the Duke. Here's one that we found particularly interesting.

CAPTAIN H.J. KIRRIN

November 16th, 1859

Your Most Honourable Duke of Dibeltoynn,

I am now certain that during the storm that took the Peregrine and your precious cargo, my navigator and a lifeboat went missing as well. It seems that the foul villain made it look as though he was lost at sea.

Your humble servant,

Captain Henry John Kirrin

The letter was straightforward enough. The Captain named his navigator as the wretched traitor who had caused his fine ship to go down. Inside the envelope, folded around the letter, was a peculiar strip of fabric with threads sewn into it to form a chequered pattern. It measured 26 boxes long and 3 boxes wide. Three of the boxes contained a sewn-in knot, and there was a roughly embroidered zigzag line connecting the knots. We all looked at each other with the same burning question in our eyes. Could this be the map that would lead us to the Royal Dragon?

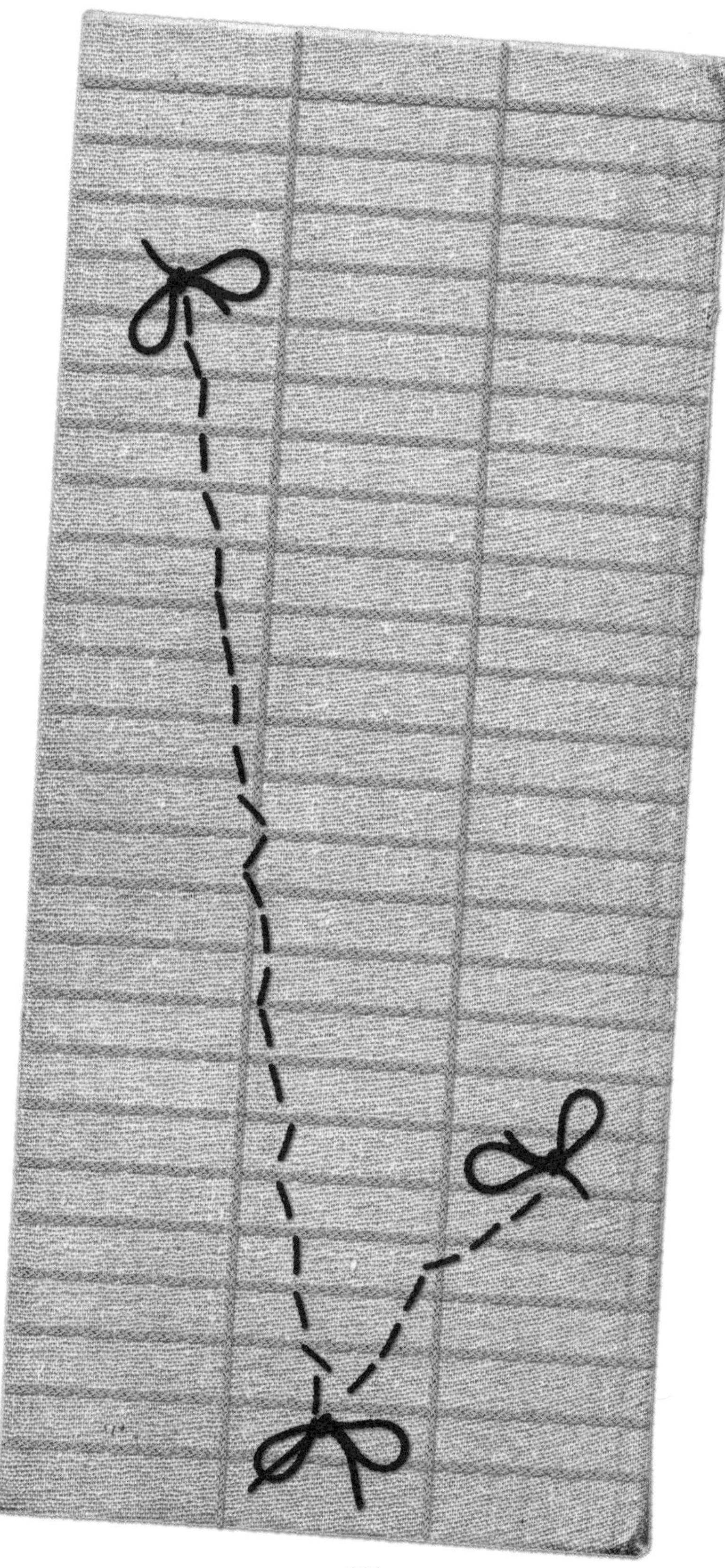

That evening, as we toasted sausages and marshmallows on our open fire, we racked our brains trading guesses about the meaning of the strange scrap of fabric.

Anne was convinced it was a map showing the Isles of Scilly on a grid system and that the *Peregrine* was wrecked in the middle of the three marked islands. The boys suggested that the zigzag line could be an arrow, or a route to follow – but they weren't sure where to. Much to everyone's surprise, it was George who solved the puzzle.

"Maybe it's simpler than all that," she mused out loud. "Maybe it's obvious. There are 26 columns. What else has 26 in it? The alphabet!" she cried, stumbling on her answer. We knew instantly that she was right and very quickly worked out what the three letters were (and hope that you have, too).

The coded map had led us to another puzzle. What did the three alphabet letters mean? Could they be part of the island's name where the *Peregrine* went down? We were desperate to learn which island we needed to explore. Julian got out his map of the Scilly Isles and we all leaned in to examine the names of each island – there were dozens. We couldn't find anything that linked the three letters to an island.

We expect you have already spotted what we did not (at least not until later). We were so focused on finding a map to the *Peregrine's* wreck that we'd convinced ourselves the scrap of fabric had to be that map.

Having carefully looked through all the papers from the Duke's secret room, we turned in for the night. It was a warm and dry evening so we laid our sleeping bags out under the stars. We knew that we were safe as long as Timmy was around. Old Tim never truly slept, instead keeping one ever-watchful eye on the rest of us, ready to protect us at the first sign of any danger. Sadly, we were about to encounter some 'dangers' that Timmy couldn't protect us from …

Anne's Diary - 23rd August, 1959

The Penzance Woodland Estate

Dear Diary,

The early rays of the morning sun woke me up. I do so love dawn in the woods. The world is covered in dew and the light from the rising sun turns everything golden and magical-looking. The others are still asleep. I'm being careful not to wake them. We've agreed to return to the Pollacks' after lunch today and George and the boys want to spend the morning in the river with Timmy. I'd rather not get wet through and frozen (the cold water takes my breath away!) so I'm going to take a short wander by myself through the woods. Bread and honey will do them for breakfast (I've already eaten mine), and I've left them a note to expect me in plenty of time for lunch.

I like taking walks in the woods by myself. It's quieter than going in a group so there's more chance of seeing animals. I've got my camera with me, and a few essential supplies. Early morning is the best time to spot the dear little animals getting ready for their day. If I'm very quiet, I should be able to see lots of things!

WOODLAND WILDLIFE

We do love trips in the country not only for the chance to get lots of lovely fresh air, but also to see all the beautiful animals and plants. There are so many wonderful things if you know where to look, Here is some information we found on a few of our favourites.

RABBIT

Small grey-brown mammal that can be anything between 12-18 inches long and can live to around 20 years old. Rabbits are most active at dusk and dawn and can often be seen between these times. The female is known as a doe and the male is called a buck. Rabbits live in medium-sized groups, in what is collectively known as a warren.

RED DEER

The largest of the wild animals found in the U.K. Red Deer were rare in some places until conservation efforts saw a growth in their population. The male, or stag, can reach 4 feet in height, and sports impressive antlers that grow up to an inch a day. These antlers can be seen at their best during the autumn. Deer are very nervous, and are most active at dawn and dusk.

BAT

There are fourteen species of bat in the U.K. and despite their useful role in controlling the insect population, eleven of them are currently on the endangered species list. A single bat can catch up to 600 mosquitoes in an hour! Bats can be seen flying around mostly at dusk, and can be recognized by their high-pitched squeaking call as they use echoes to hunt out prey and to find their way.

BADGER

The easily recognized black and white faced mammal is rarely seen due to its nocturnal habits. Badgers live in groups of up to twelve members, collectively know as clans. They can reach up to fifteen years of age, although three is the average lifespan. Badgers live on everything from berries and earthworms to eggs and reptiles.

BARN OWL

The edges of woodland may reveal the chance to see the extremely elegant Barn Owl. These pale nocturnal hunters feed mainly on rodents and pound for pound consume more of them than any other animal. The owl's silent flight aids its hearing-based hunting skills allowing it to strike suddenly through long grass, and even snow, with deadly accuracy.

FOX

The species indigenous to the U.K. is called the Red Fox - although its actual markings are a red coat with white underbelly. The fox can run at speeds of up to 45mph and has cat-like agility to aid it in its search for prey. Their primary diet consists of rodents, amphibians and fish, although they have been known to kill deer fawns on occasion.

ADDER

Britain's only poisonous snake is a member of the viper family and their bites can be painful but are rarely fatal. Colours vary from a light brown with diamond patterning down the back, to almost black with no discernible markings. The viper is a timid creature and will shy away from human contact.

HEDGEHOG

Hedgehogs have changed little over the last 15 million years. Despite the common practice of putting milk out, hedgehogs are actually lactose-intolerant even though they will readily consume cheese and milk which make them ill. Their natural diet is insects, earthworms, berries and fruit.

SPARROWHAWK

The sparrowhawk is common in rural areas across Britain, as well as Northern Europe and Asia, and migrates as far as North Africa during the winter months. A bird-hunting hawk from the same family as the eagle and buzzard, the sparrowhawk is a surprise attacker launching at its prey from treetops and hedges. It can often be seen watching for targets from high vantage points. The original name for a male was a musket. The famous gun was actually named after the bird!

SQUIRREL

The common grey squirrel can be found all over Britain and has spread with such veracity that it has almost wiped out the indigenous red squirrel in all but a few areas. Squirrels spend the majority of the year hoarding food, and it is estimated that one squirrel can have several thousand stores to see it through times when food is scarce.

All photographs courtesy of Anne Kirrin.

CARE FOR THE COUNTRYSIDE

Spending time in the countryside with all the wonderful animals and plants is such an enjoyable thing to do, but there are certain rules that you really must follow. These rules will help protect the animals who live there, and also make sure that all the sights, sounds and smells remain for everyone to enjoy for a long time to come. We've listed some of the rules you should be following for a happier and healthier countryside for all.

Respect, Protect, Enjoy

BE SAFE - PLAN AHEAD AND FOLLOW ANY SIGNS

Even if you know the area you are visiting, always be prepared for the unexpected and pay attention to any warning or information signs you see. These signs are there for a reason and protect you, the plants and the animals who live there.

KEEP TO PUBLIC PATHS ACROSS FARMLAND

Farmers' crops cost a lot of money and take a long time to grow, and their livelihood might depend on the animals they keep. The last thing they want is people walking all over their crops, or scaring their sheep or cows. Keep to the paths marked, or if no paths are available keep to the edge of a field rather than walking straight across it.

USE GATES AND STILES TO CROSS FENCES, HEDGES AND WALLS

Don't just climb over fences as you may damage them. The fences are often there to keep farm animals safe, and if these fences are broken the animals could get out and possibly hurt themselves. It also costs the farmers a lot to repair damaged fences.

LEAVE GATES AS YOU FIND THEM

Farmers often leave gates closed to keep sheep or cows in one place. Sometimes however, they leave gates open to allow the animals access to other fields, or to reach food or water. Make sure you close any gates you open; farm animals roaming freely can be dangerous for other walkers, and for the animals themselves!

KEEP DOGS UNDER CONTROL

Your dog may love to explore the countryside (Timmy certainly does!) and it can be great fun to have dogs with you on walks, as long as they obey the rules too. If dogs are allowed to run wild they can cause untold damage to crops and they can also hurt or scare other animals. Letting dogs off the lead is allowed, just ensure you keep them under control. Don't forget to clean up anything your dog may leave behind, too!

HELP TO KEEP WATER CLEAN

Streams and rivers provide vital drinking water for country animals such as mice and rabbits. The water might also be used by farmers for their livestock and may even feed local reservoirs. Pollution is not only wrong it's illegal. Do everything you can to avoid polluting any water you find.

LEAVE LIVESTOCK, CROPS AND MACHINERY ALONE

Farm machinery can be very dangerous, and easily broken if you don't know how to use it. The general rule is look but don't touch, and that goes for crops and farm animals too. No matter how cute the animals might be, do not go up to them. Animals can be unpredictable and may bite or cause other injuries, especially if they are scared. If an animal looks frightened or hurt, do not approach it. Instead inform the farmer who owns the land.

TAKE YOUR LITTER HOME

Keep anywhere you visit clean and tidy. Litter is not only horrible to look at but can also pose a risk to the farm animals and wildlife who live in the country. Take all of your rubbish home with you and keep the countryside a clean, beautiful and safe place to be!

DON'T DISTURB OR DAMAGE WILDLIFE OR HISTORIC PLACES

The countryside and historic places are there for everyone's enjoyment and damaging them only spoils things for others. The only reason you can enjoy it now is because the person before you did not destroy it. The pretty plant you pick up, or the interesting rock you take home, might look nice on your windowsill, but it could be some little animal's home! Remember, take only pictures and leave only footprints.

PROTECT WILDLIFE, PLANTS AND TREES

Destroying things in the countryside not only ruins the enjoyment of others but can also have an impact on the environment. Damaging plants might mean that you are destroying a wild deer's evening meal, or a ladybird's habitat. If you forage for food make sure you don't strip an area bare. Leaving nothing behind may stop it from growing again, and remember that animals need that food too!

GUARD AGAINST FIRE

Make sure you put out any camp fires thoroughly. Do not leave burning embers, drop matches or cause any hazard that may start or encourage a fire. If you see any fires burning out of control contact the emergency services immediately and do not try to tackle the blaze yourself.

Take only pictures, leave only footprints

The rest of us woke up to find Anne's note but we weren't worried. We had camped together a lot by then and knew that Anne was happy and comfortable in the woods. As long as she didn't walk too far, she would be fine on her own. We knew she didn't much like the water and after a quick breakfast that's exactly where we headed. It was such fun to have the river all to ourselves and Timmy lost no time in jumping straight in. We followed after him and spent a wonderful morning swimming and playing together.

George and Dick took turns to see who could hold their breath for the longest time underwater while Julian floated lazily on his back. Finally, we were all tired out (Timmy had made us throw sticks into the river for him to fetch at least a hundred times!) and headed back to camp.

Anne hadn't returned when we got back so we dried off, dressed and prepared a hearty lunch. We were ravenous! We made cheese sandwiches with thickly cut bread and set out tomatoes, apples, a huge cake that Mrs Pollack baked for us early yesterday, and bottles of ginger beer. Saving some of everything for Anne (and still expecting her to walk into camp at any moment), we tucked in. The outdoors did make us so hungry, especially Timmy.

By early afternoon, we were all anxious about Anne. She had set off at the break of day, with nothing but a flask of water and a light snack. There was no other explanation – Anne was lost in the forest!

"We've got to search for her," said Julian. We set out immediately.

Oh, dear! I'm afraid that I've been awfully stupid and got myself lost! I followed a butterfly into the woods and didn't pay any attention to where I was going. Silly, silly mistake! Oh, but I was having such a nice walk. I've seen lots of birds and I even caught a glimpse of a deer! I climbed to the top of a ridge – what a breathtaking view! Now I'm sitting on a fallen tree and I daren't move for fear of losing myself deeper in the forest. I wish now that I'd stayed with the others.

Now Anne, don't panic. Do as Julian would: keep calm and think what to do. Make a plan. I must try to retrace my steps somehow. I'll call to the others. If I've not wandered too far, perhaps Timmy will hear me.

HOW TO AVOID GETTING LOST

Every adventurer needs to know their location at all times. If you find yourself lost in the wilderness without a compass or a map, there are things you can do to get back to familiar ground.

LANDMARKS

01. Pay attention to any local landmarks or points of interest.
02. Landmarks don't have to be major buildings or constructions, they may be as simple as rocky outcroppings that catch your attention, or even trees and shrubs.
03. Make sure you note down on which side you pass any memorable sights. This will aid you if you need to retrace your steps.

LEAVE A TRAIL

01. When you make a turn on a path or change direction, make small piles of rocks or fallen leaves to mark where you have been. That way, you can follow these back should the need arise.
02. Try not to make slashes in trees or bend branches if you can help it as this could damage the tree.

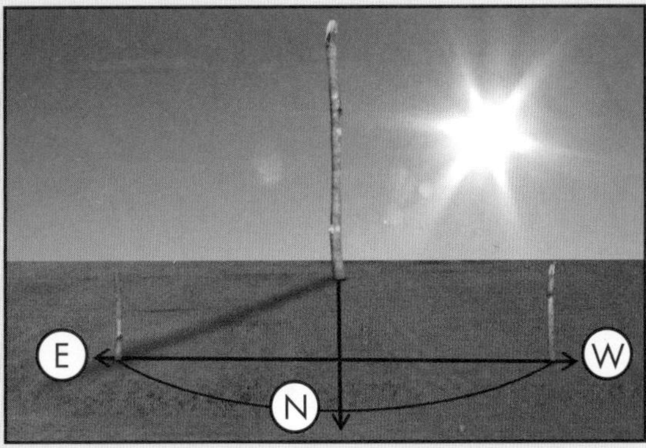

FIND DIRECTION WITHOUT A COMPASS

01. Push a long stick into the ground.
02. Mark the end of the stick's shadow in the dirt.
03. Wait about half an hour and mark the end of the second shadow.
04. As the sun moves west, the shadow will move east. Now that you know where east and west lie it is a simple matter of deduction to find north and south.

EMERGENCY SURVIVAL KIT

You don't have to carry your whole pack on a short hike, but it is sensible to carry a small emergency case like this one filled with vital items you may need if you get lost.

BAG
A strong, waterproof but lightweight bag is ideal for carrying all the items in your emergency kit.

BANDAGE
A small well-wrapped bandage is essential for dealing with any unforeseen injuries or sprains. Can also be useful in place of rope or string for securing shelters etc.

KNIFE
A good quality utility knife can be a lifesaver in more ways than one and can be vital when making fires or searching for food.

WHISTLE
For emergency signalling for help. Make sure you learn how to send the right signals.

SUNSCREEN
Sunburn is not fun at any time, even more uncomfortable if you are in a survival situation. Sunburn can lead to pain and dehydration that can only make matters worse. Apply well and apply regularly is the key.

WATER PURIFICATION TABLETS
A time-saver and a must have if you are in tropical climes. Check your local camping or outdoor supplies store.

MATCHES
Waterproof matches are the best, if you can't get them make sure you keep them in a waterproof bag or container. There's nothing worse than soggy matches when you need them most.

WHAT TO DO IF YOU DO GET LOST

Despite all your planning and practice you find yourself lost in the wilderness. Which way do you turn? Will you ever be found? What is the best way to find your way out?

BASIC SAFETY

01. Before you set out make sure you inform someone of your expected route and return time. Help cannot be sent if nobody is expecting you back at a certain time.

02. Check the weather closely before you set out, the last thing you want is to be trapped somewhere you don't know, in the fog and rain, with no idea how to get back.

03. If you know that search parties may be heading your way it is best to stay where you are. Moving away from your position could cause more work for search parties and there is a higher chance that you will not be found.

RETRACE YOUR STEPS

01. Mark the place where you first realized you were lost.

02. Trace your footprints back in the direction you have just walked. Stop and see if anything looks familiar.

03. If anything does look familiar, mark that new spot and continue to trace your trail back. Keep marking familiar spots so you can track your progress.

04. Make a large, easily recognizable mark at each junction on a trail or a change of direction, these can be vital if you make a wrong turn and need to backtrack at all.

DON'T PANIC

01. Panicking causes your brain to stop working properly.

02. Panic can cause you to lose your bearings completely and makes retracing your steps extremely difficult.

03. Panic may even turn into shock or even physical harm from poorly thought out decisions.

MAKE NOISE

01. People may be searching for you. Use anything you can to make a noise.

02. Using your voice will not carry as well as banging a tree or blowing a whistle, it will also reduce your strength which could be vital, depending on how long you are lost for.

03. Remember the international rule of three when calling for help and make all of your noises in three sharp bursts.

BE AWARE OF THE TIME OF DAY

If you're lost in the woods, it's important to be able to judge how many daylight hours you have left. If there's any chance that you will still be lost when the sun goes down, you will need to move quickly and set up an emergency camp while it's still light.

TELLING THE TIME WITHOUT A WATCH

01. Note which direction is east from your current position (before noon the sun will be closest to the eastern horizon and furthest away after noon.)

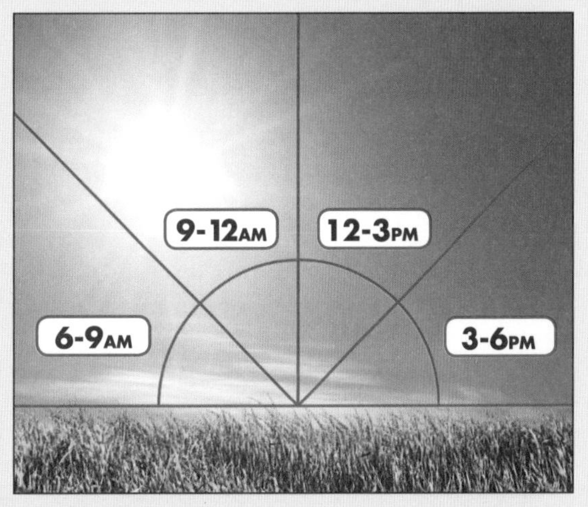

02. Divide the sky into four imaginary equal segments from one horizon to the other. Each of these segments will represent three hours.

03. If you know the time the sun rose on the day in question you can get a more accurate reading. For example, if the sun rose at 6am and is still in the first of your four segments it is between six and nine. If it is in the second of your segments it is between 9 and 12am.

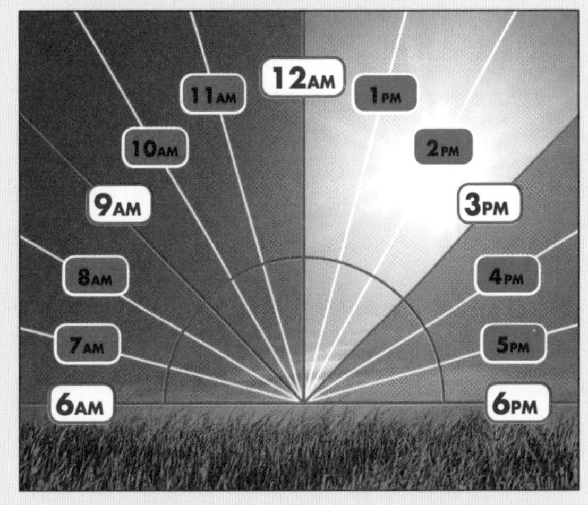

04. You can get an even closer reading by dividing each of your segments up into a further three parts to represent each hour.

HOW TO TRACK A TRAIL

Find your foe faster

You are convinced the wrongdoers you are following are ahead of you. With no sight of them you need to be certain you are still on the right track. It's time to put some tracking skills into practice!

TIME MATTERS

01. The time of day can have an effect on what you see.
02. The late hours of the day are best for tracking as the sun casts a shadow on tracks, making them easier to see.
03. If tracking at night keep low to the ground, and use a torch to help highlight footprints on the ground.
04. How old is the print?
    There are a few ways to tell:
    • Has the sun dried it out or is the print still slightly damp?
    • Has the wind smoothed out the edges of the print?
    • When looking for trodden down grass remember that it will return to its original standing state in around 24 hours.

FOOTPRINTS

01. Look for footprints in patches of sandy or wet ground. Get down low and turn your head to look at an angle.
02. Measure the footprints you find with a tape measure and note their dimensions. This will give a reference point to ensure you follow the right tracks.
03. Measure the distance between each track. This will help you to determine the stride length. It will also tell you whether the person you are following was running or walking, the longer the stride the faster they are moving. The deeper the indentation the more pressure your target is putting into their step. This also indicates running or carrying a heavy load or person.
04. If tracking animals remember to look for and identify droppings. Only handle animal droppings if wearing disposable gloves as many contain microbes that can be dangerous.
05. Invest in a detailed animal track guide. This will make it easier to tell the difference between various animal tracks, and how to identify their varying prints based on their movement patterns.

TRAIL CLUES

- Keep your eyes open for hair or fabric snagged on branches or fences.
- Carry tweezers, clear tape, and plastic bags to collect any evidence.
- A magnifying glass can be useful for close examination and comparison of anything you find.
- Look for bent or broken tree branches and tall grass that has been pushed down or walked on. These are signs that the person may have gone off the main trail.
- Keep an eye out for anything that looks out of the ordinary such as overturned stones, mud marks on rocks and logs, and broken cobwebs.

CAST AND KEEP

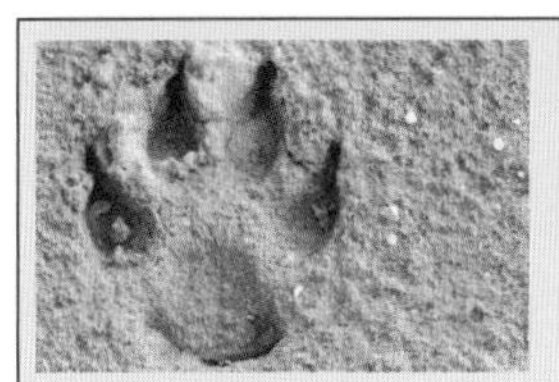

You will need:

- **Plaster of Paris**
- **Talcum powder**
- **Lolly sticks**

01. Use the lolly sticks to make a square around the foot print.
02. Mix the plaster following the instructions on the packet.
03. Sprinkle talcum powder on the print. This will help the plaster to stick to the print.
04. Pour the plaster around the outside of the print so it flows slowly into the print. Do not pour the plaster straight onto the print as the force of the plaster flow would ruin the print.
05. When the print is half full with plaster, stop pouring and put some lolly sticks into the plaster. This will make the cast stronger.
06. Pour in the rest of the plaster and wait for about half an hour.
07. When the cast is hard, carefully pry it out of the ground.
08. Wait for 24 hours to allow the plaster to set. Then gently clean it with a soft brush.

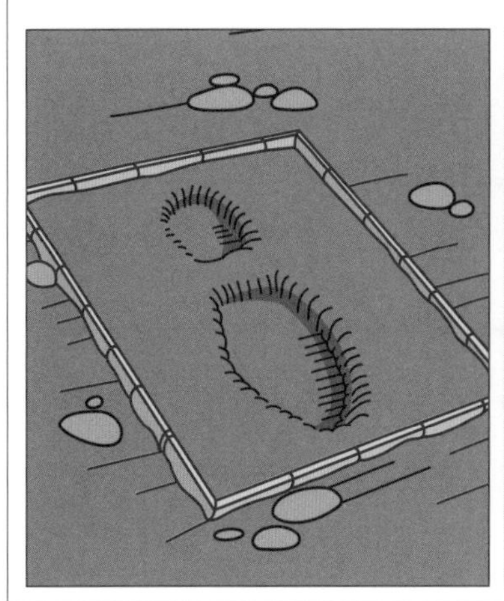

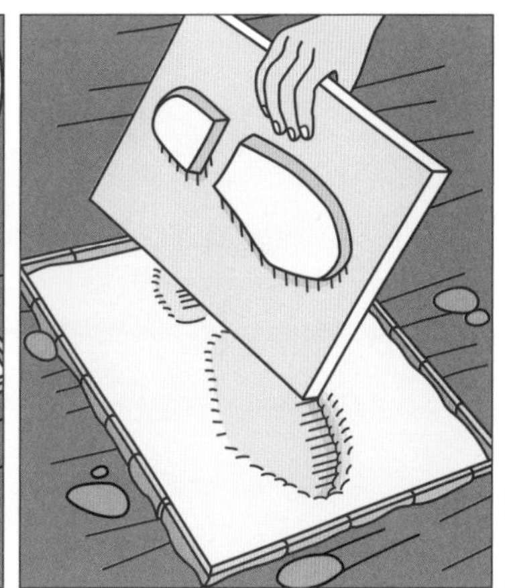

Julian led the search for Anne, telling the others that it was "time to put all our tracking abilities to the test". We were suddenly very grateful for the rain that had fallen the other day – it would help us to see Anne's footprints in the moist ground.

We followed the riverbank and saw Anne's handkerchief lying in the weeds on the other side. The boys were deep in discussion about how to cross the river when they heard a sharp bark.

"Timmy's quite right," said George. "We mustn't stand here talking things through! We must get across and find our Anne. We can see that she's been at that spot and I'll bet Timmy can pick up her scent from there."

Anne would be worried and frightened. We had to find her as soon as possible. Julian looked at his map. It showed a small bridge a mile down river that Anne must have used to get across. There was a path on the other side of the river that ran back up the riverbank. Anne's handkerchief was lying next to this path.

"You're right, George. We don't have time to walk to the bridge. We need to cross the river here," said Julian.

"It's pretty shallow. I'm sure we can wade across safely," said George.

Here's how to cross a river – exactly the way George showed Julian and Dick to do it that day.

Photograph courtesy of Anne Kirrin.

HOW TO CROSS A RIVER

Hot on the trail, you find the only way forwards is blocked by a river. Going around will take too long and the nearest bridge has collapsed in a storm, so your only choice is to take the risky route of crossing it.

WARNING

FIND THE BEST POSSIBLE PLACE TO CROSS

01. Cross at the river's widest point. It will be the shallowest and slowest part of the river.

02. Avoid rocky areas. The rocks can be slippery and dangerous.

TEST THE DEPTH OF THE RIVER AND THE STRENGTH OF ITS CURRENT

01. Use a long stick to test how deep the river is. Remember, the river is deeper in the middle than at the banks.

02. If the river is deeper than your knees and the water pushes at your legs, bubbling and swirling, the river is too strong and it is dangerous to cross.

03. Float a stick down stream. Watch to see how fast the stick travels. A fast moving river can be difficult and dangerous to cross. Remember, a river's current is faster in the middle than at the banks.

04. As you cross the river, keep using a long stick to test its depth. Don't lean on the stick for support, you can easily slip and fall.

CROSS THE RIVER WITH YOUR WALKING SHOES ON

01. As long as you are wearing sensible footwear, it is better to keep your shoes on.

02. Shoes will help your feet get a firmer hold on the riverbed, and protect them from the sharp edges of stones that may be on the bottom and can cause serious injury.

DON'T GET ALL YOUR THINGS WET

01. Pack up your things in a waterproof bag and hang this on your back or hold it above your head.

02. Roll up your trouser legs or take them off and put them in your pack. Wet trousers will add extra weight and could make crossing difficult.

DON'T TIE A ROPE AROUND ANYONE'S WAIST

01. If they slip and fall, the rope will drag the person under and could well take you with them.

KEEP YOUR FEET WIDE APART AND SHUFFLE THROUGH THE WATER

01. Don't pick your feet up while walking across the river. You need to keep both feet on the river bottom, otherwise the current can easily knock you over.

02. Cross the river at an angle and facing the current.

03. Shuffle sideways steadily like a tennis player moving across the court.

IF YOU FALL IN

01. It is very important to get warm and dry as quickly as possible. Build a fire and change into dry clothes.

02. Staying in wet clothes will make you cold, and that can lead to hypothermia (see page 143).

03. Hypothermia happens when your body temperature drops too far below normal. It can cause you to go into shock and even die.

We successfully crossed the river. As we gathered on the opposite bank, we heard the loud sound of rocks banging together, over and over again. We shouted HEY to Anne and, thank goodness, she shouted HEY back!

Anne ran out and hugged us all one by one. "I am so sorry I put you all through this," she said.

"That's all right, little sister," said Dick. "We're just glad you're unharmed! You have certainly learned a few good lessons in the forest today!"

"Let's head back to camp and get the fire going again," urged Julian. "There's not enough daylight left to be travelling back tonight and I think we could all do with a cup of hot cocoa."

"And you can have your lunch, Anne," George pitched in. "You must be famished. We saved you some, you know. Not even Timmy tried to eat your share!"

Timmy barked and barked. We were all frightfully relieved to be the Five together again. We would camp out an extra night and return to the Pollacks' tomorrow. Well, that was the plan anyway. Of course, sometimes even the best-laid plans can go awry. As you'll see …

The following morning (being the 24th of August, 1959), we made a breakfast of some tinned sardines and some more of Mrs Pollack's delicious bread. We were glad that Julian had brought some emergency supplies (even if you're only planning one night in the woods, it pays to be prepared). We set about dismantling our camp. Julian insisted that we leave the forest as we found it so we spread all our firewood around and stamped earth on to the spot where we'd built our fire.

Julian looked at his map and found a short cut back to the path that would take us to the Pollacks' old, thatched cottage. So, with compass in hand, Julian led us through the woods. After walking for two or so hours, we found that the forest floor was becoming wetter and wetter. We were hiking on the edge of a swamp.

Two mallards quacked nearby and caught Timmy's attention. He took off after the ducks and George immediately ran after him. Timmy jumped into the murky swamp just as the ducks flew off and out of reach of his snapping teeth. Timmy neatly paddled back to us, but George wasn't so lucky. She was stuck in a bog hole and couldn't move her feet!

"Help!" cried George. "I'm sinking!"

HOW TO ESCAPE FROM A BOG OR QUICKSAND

While tracking a clue you quickly find yourself sinking into what appeared to be solid ground. Forget all the films you've seen, all the myths about quicksand being inescapable are false. Stay calm and it could save your life.

AVOID UNSTABLE GROUND

01. Quicksand is most likely to occur along beaches, the edges of marshes, rivers and river estuaries.
02. Always try to carry a long stick with you so you can test ground that appears to be unstable.

KEEP CALM

01. If you do start to sink, drop everything you are carrying as the more you can reduce your weight, the slower you will sink
02. Above all do not panic as sudden movements and struggling will only pull you deeper.
03. Breathing deeply will not only allow you to stay calm, but also increase your buoyancy.
04. While trying to free yourself take plenty of breaks without moving, you will need all your strength to get out.

SHALLOW SURVIVAL

01. If you find yourself sinking, but have only sunk a small way in, keep your head up and crawl off the surface of the quicksand on your hands and knees.
02. If you are still sinking lie on your stomach to spread your weight and wriggle your way out like a snake.
03. Spread out your body as much as possible to distribute your weight and if possible get someone to throw you a line and pull you out.

DEEPER DANGER

01. If the quicksand reaches higher than your knees, lay your pole horizontally behind you and try to lie back onto it to help distribute your weight evenly. This will help you pull your feet out. You can now slide your way across the pole to safety.
02. Freeing your legs is easier than you think. Make circular motions with your legs to allow more water into the quicksand making it more fluid and easier to pull your legs free.
03. Don't worry about losing your shoes as bare feet are actually more useful in this situation.

ROPE TO THE RESCUE

01. If a rope is available make sure it is of sufficient length so the person throwing it can safely stand on solid ground to help pull you out.
02. If the person throwing the rope is not strong enough to pull you out, tie the rope to a tree or secure object so you can pull yourself out.

HOW TO THROW A LIFELINE

Your friend is sinking quickly and you're the only one who can help. It's time to put your rope to use and throw them a line. A life may depend on it so make sure you get in plenty of practice.

01. Secure one end of the rope to something sturdy, like a tree.
02. Coil the rope into two sections, so that you have a coil of rope in each hand.
03. Hold the coil that is closest to the secured end of the rope in your left hand. The other coiled section is in your right hand (or vice-versa if you are left-handed.)
04. Swing your arms back and forth a few times to build momentum.
05. Throw the right-hand coil first, aiming for it to land beyond the person you are trying to help.
06. Throw the coil up and out so the rope can extend a good distance. As the first coil spreads out, release the coil from your left hand.
07. Practise throwing coiled rope this way at home by trying to throw the rope at a target. If there's an emergency, you'll already know how to throw someone a lifeline.

Dick threw a lifeline out to George and while she held on, Timmy, Dick and Julian pulled her out of the bog – thank goodness! She was unharmed but soaked through and quite muddy. We hiked past the swamp and rested in a clearing to eat almost the last of our food – a little bread and cheese and some apples. George dried off in the sun.

Back on the trail, we started descending a hill. It was steeper than Julian had imagined and we were moving rather quickly. Suddenly Anne lost her footing and began to slip down the steep hill. Dick turned and caught hold of Anne, steadying her on her feet. Poor Dick, he stopped Anne from falling but he badly twisted his ankle in the process.

What bad luck! First Anne, then George and now Dick! Julian told him to try walking on it, but he couldn't. George tested Dick's ankle for breaks and thankfully found none. Julian had Dick sit down and take off his shoe. Then he carefully elevated Dick's foot by placing a bag under it. George took out her first aid kit and selected a clean cloth. She soaked it in the cool river and wrapped it around Dick's ankle to stop the swelling. Though he would never say so, we could tell that Dick was in quite a bit of pain.

"What are we going to do, Julian? Can we carry Dick all the way back to the cottage?" asked Anne.

"No, I'm afraid not, old girl. He's too heavy," (he smiled at Dick when he said that), "and it's too far. We'll need to camp out again tonight so that Dick can recover. We'll head back tomorrow."

"But Julian!" cried Anne. "We're already a day late getting back to the Pollacks'. They'll be frightfully worried about us!"

"Can't be helped, old girl," said Julian and turned his attention back to Dick's predicament.

George took out a roll of elastic bandage and expertly wrapped Dick's ankle. George knows her first aid. And you should too.

FIRST AID

No adventurer should set foot outside their own door without knowing at least some basic first-aid. You never know what you will have to deal with while on an adventure.

Essential first aid information is given here but should not be used as a substitute for professional training by recognized first aid organizations such as the Red Cross. For more information visit your nearest Red Cross centre. Or go to www.redcross.org.

BLISTERS

01. A blister provides a natural protection against bacteria, and it shouldn't be punctured unless it is painful.

02. If the blister needs to be punctured use a sterilized needle, and puncture around the edges of the sore.

03. A small blister can be covered with a normal adhesive plaster, or a specially designed blister plaster.

04. For larger blisters use a bandage that absorbs any moisture that might ooze from the sore.

BURNS

01. For larger burns you will need to seek medical help immediately. Only minor burns can be treated yourself. Place the affected area under cold, running water. If you don't have access to running water, or the burn is in an area that makes this difficult, sponge cold water onto the area instead.

02. Always use cold water and do not be tempted to use ice or cream on a burn. Cold water helps reduce the heat whereas ice can cause frostbite and burn cream can work with the heat to 'cook' the skin.

03. Try not to apply any pressure to the affected area, loosely cover it with a clean bandage or gauze. Do not use a material which could stick to the wound if it seeps or oozes.

04. For larger and more serious burns cool the area with a damp cold cloth until professional help arrives.

CARDIO PULMONARY RESUSCITATION (CPR)

01. Roll your patient onto their back on a flat, firm surface. (If you think that they could possibly have injured their neck or back, roll their head and shoulders at the same time.)

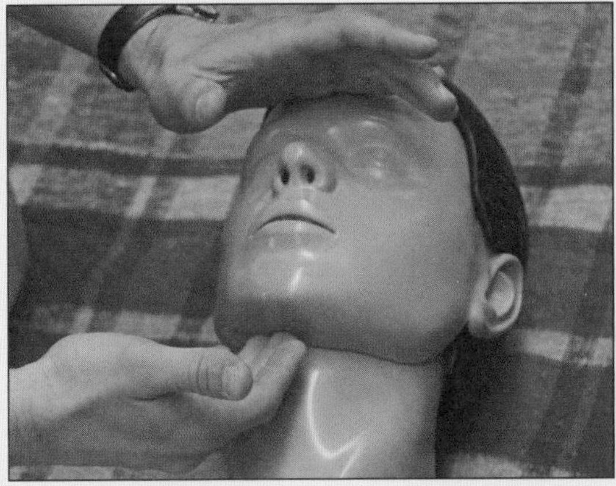

02. Place one hand on your patient's forehead, and with the other lift their chin. Look into their throat to make sure that the airway is clear.

03. When breathing normally, a person's chest will rise and you will be able to hear breath sounds. If this is not the case with your patient you will need to begin CPR immediately.

04. To ensure your breath goes into the patient's lungs, and does not escape, make sure their chin is tilted upwards and their head back. Check your mouth is completely over the patient's and hold their nose.

05. Take a normal breath and exhale into the person's mouth for one second. This is known as a rescue breath.

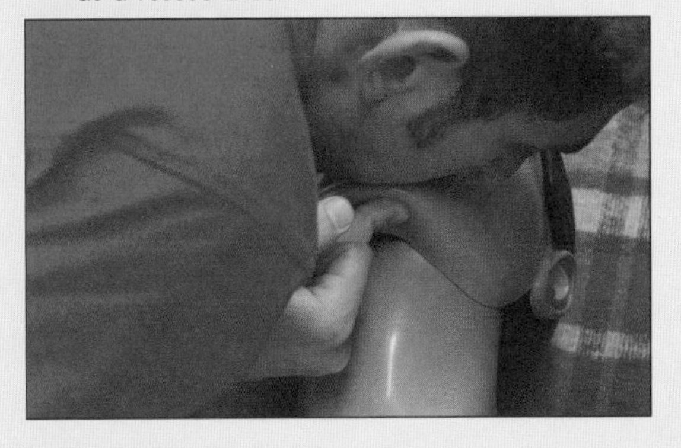

05. Check to see that the chest rises. If the chest does not rise, check the patient's airway again before giving a second rescue breath.

06. Watch to see the chest rise again. If the patient is still having trouble receiving the breaths check for a pulse before moving on to compressions.

COMPRESSIONS

01. Remove thick or restrictive clothing so you can see the patient's chest move. Place one hand with two fingers at the end of the breastbone where the ribs come together.

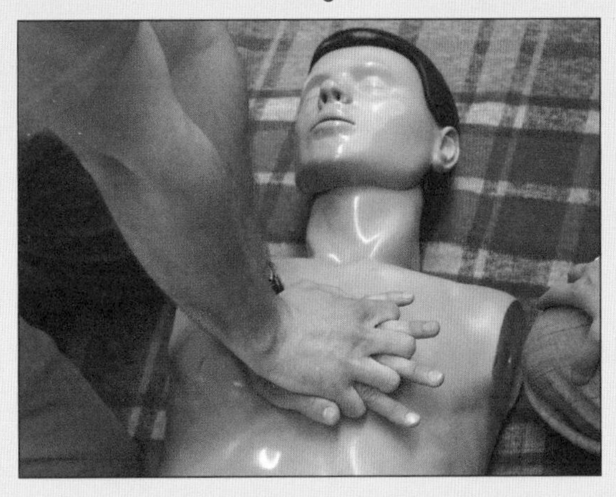

02. Place the other hand on top, lacing your fingers together and raising them, so the palms of your hands are doing the work. Your shoulders should be directly over your hands, with your arms straight and elbows locked.

03. Press down on the patient's chest, using your body weight. The force should push the breastbone down 1.5–2 inches (5 cm).

04. Allow the chest to re-inflate after each compression. Give 30 compressions at around 100–120 compressions a minute.

05. Once you have delivered 30 compressions give two more rescue breaths, remembering to clear the patient's air way.

06. Keep repeating the sequence of 30 compressions and two breaths until trained medical staff arrives, or until the person is breathing normally.

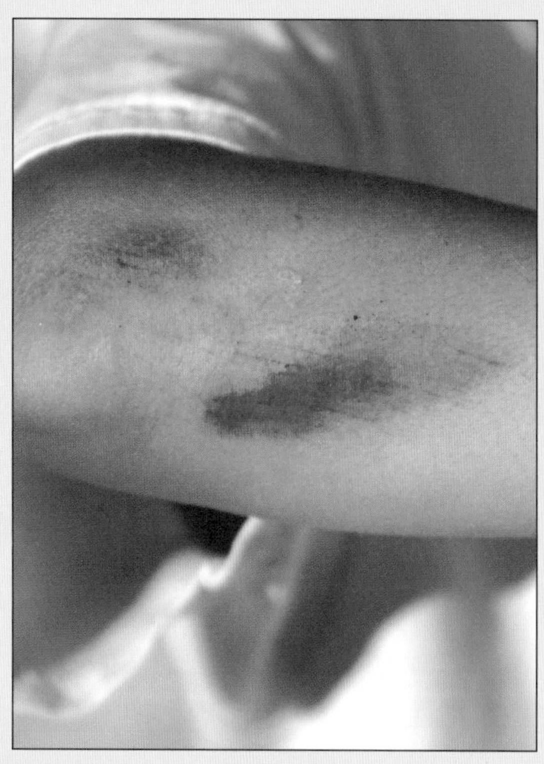

CUTS AND SCRAPES

01. Small cuts and grazes will not need any further treatment than being cleaned. But larger, more serious, wounds might not stop bleeding without care.

02. To help stop the bleeding, apply pressure on either side of the wound for around 25 minutes. Covering the cut with a clean cloth or gauze while pressing down can also help.

03. Flush the wound by running clean, clear water over it. If there is anything still in the wound carefully remove it using sterilized tweezers.

04. Gently apply some antiseptic cream or ointment to the wound. This helps stop the area becoming infected.

05. A graze or scrape is best left open to the air, as is a wound that is already healing. Only fresh, open wounds should be covered, preferably with a clean cloth or bandage to help keep them clean and reduce the risk of infection.

06. Change the dressing every day, or when it becomes unclean. This helps further to avoid infection.

07. For deeper or larger wounds stitches might be necessary, so it is advisable to seek medical attention as soon as possible. In emergency situations, use medical tape to help close the cut until you can reach help.

CHOKING

THE HEIMLICH MANOEUVRE

01. Position yourself behind your patient and wrap your arms around their waist as if you are going to give them a hug.

02. Lean forward slightly so the patient is gently tilting.

03. Clench one hand into a fist and place it just below the patient's ribs but above their belly button.

04. Wrap your other hand around the first. Pull inwards with a sharp upwards movement, as if you are trying to pick the patient up.

05. If the blockage is not removed repeat the action.

FAINTING

01. Lie the patient on their back and gently raise their legs so that they are above the level of the patient's heart.

02. Place one hand on your patient's forehead, and with the other lift their chin. Look into their throat to make sure that the airway is clear.

03. If the patient is not breathing you may need to start CPR.

04. If breathing is normal help try to restore the blood flow. Ensure the patient's clothing is loose, and gently elevate their legs above the level of their head.

HYPOTHERMIA

SYMPTOMS

- Shaking and shivering
- Confusion and loss of concentration
- Slow, shallow breathing
- Drowsiness, lethargy or weakness
- Low body temperature or cold, clammy skin.

01. Try to keep the patient warm. Move them out of any obvious drafts and wind, and keep them wrapped warmly, particularly the patient's head.

02. If the patient's clothing is wet remove it immediately and replace it with dry clothing, or blankets.

03. Do not try to increase the patient's body temperature too quickly. Using hot water, or sources of heat such as heat lamps can cause shock.

04. Focus on warming the patient's chest and waist area to increase the flow of warm blood around the body. Warming the extremities can push cold blood back towards the organs and lead to a further drop in core body temperature.

05. A patient with hypothermia is at high risk of cardiac arrest. Therefore they must be treated gently; do not rub or massage them hoping to increase blood flow and do not offer them alcoholic drinks.

FRACTURES

01. If the patient has an open fracture (one where the skin is torn) it is important to clean the wound and stop any bleeding.

02. The injured limb should be supported and immobilized. Do not try to reset the bone, but apply a makeshift splint to help stop movement and any further damage.

03. Raise the injured limb to above the level of the heart to help reduce swelling and apply an ice pack if possible.

04. Check movement around the fracture and treat for shock by lying the patient down with their legs higher than their head.

SPRAINS

Remember the basic rules of R.I.C.E.

01. **R**est. The injured limb should be rested, but some use of the muscles is important to prevent muscle deterioration.

02. **I**ce. Cool the area as soon as possible after injury. This will help prevent swelling.

03. **C**ompress. Keeping pressure on the injured limb can also reduce swelling.

04. **E**levate. Raising the injured limb helps stop the area becoming further inflamed.

SEEK URGENT MEDICAL ATTENTION IF:

- A popping sound was heard when the injury occurred. This may mean a torn ligament rather than just a sprain.
- The area is red and hot and the patient develops a fever. This could indicate an infection.
- No improvement in the injury is made in three days.

HOW TO CARRY AN INJURED ADVENTURER

Miles from safety and injury befalls one of your party. You could decide to leave them while you go for help, but if their injuries aren't extensive, and you don't have far to go, you'll be better off carrying them yourself. Here's how to do it.

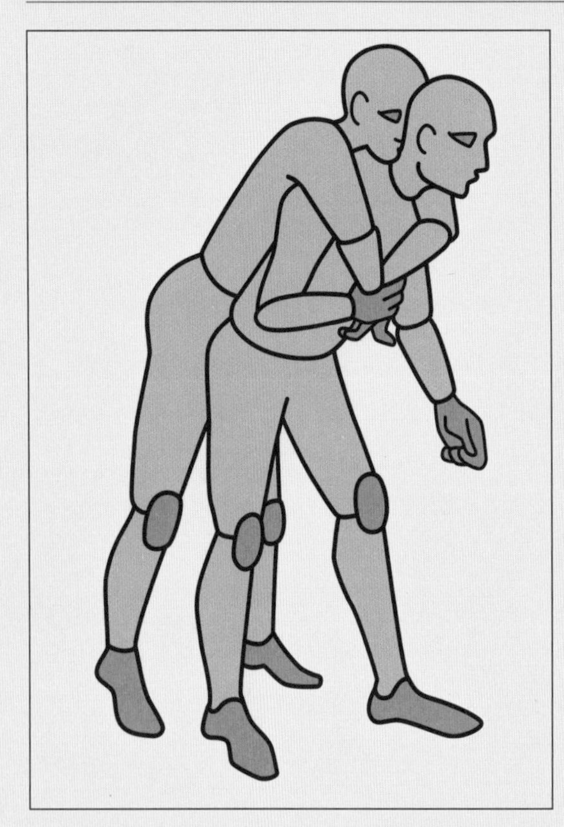

PACK CARRY

The pack carry is an excellent technique for moving someone with minor injuries over a short distance. The pack carry should not be used if you suspect the injured person has any back or spinal injury.

01. Position the injured person with their knees bent and their feet flat on the floor.

02. Stand on the injured person's feet so that the front half of your feet cover the front half of theirs.

03. Bend at the knees and cross your wrists so the injured person can grab your left hand with their right and your right hand with their left.

04. Straighten your knees so that the injured person begins to rise and straighten their legs, remember to keep your back straight and try to do it one smooth movement.

05. When they are almost in standing position twist your body in an anti-clockwise direction. Remember to keep hold of the injured person's hands as you turn.

06. As you continue to twist lift the injured person's arms over your head so that their arms form a cross above your head.

07. With your back to the injured party put your head between their arms so that their arms become crossed on your chest and your back is towards them.

08. Lean forward pulling down on their arms until their feet leave the ground, walk forward carrying them like a rucksack.

SEAT CARRY

The seat carry is a good way to move someone who is conscious and can sit up and hold on. Two people carrying together creates a strong and secure seat to carry an injured adventurer.

01. Grasp your friend's right arm just above the wrist with your right hand.

02. Use your left hand to grab the other person's left arm just above the wrist.

03. Get the other person to grab your left arm with their left hand in the same way as step one.

04. Now they need to grasp your right arm with their right hand.

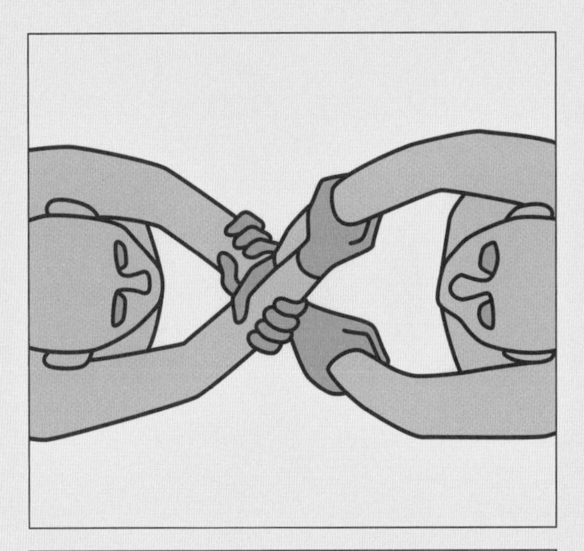

05. Bend at the knees and allow the injured party to sit on your makeshift 'seat'.

06. Take the strain on your arms before rising, remembering to keep your back straight.

07. Remember to take regular breaks while carrying to avoid dropping the injured person.

LITTER CARRY

If the person you are transporting cannot support themselves, or is in too much pain, the only option may be a makeshift stretcher or litter.

BUILD YOUR STRETCHER

01. Find two straight sturdy branches or poles that will not break under the weight.

02. Lay two shirts on the ground with their backs on the floor, buttons open and collars at opposite ends.

03. Thread the poles down each side of the shirts passing them through the sleeves.

04. Button the shirts up fully to complete your stretcher.

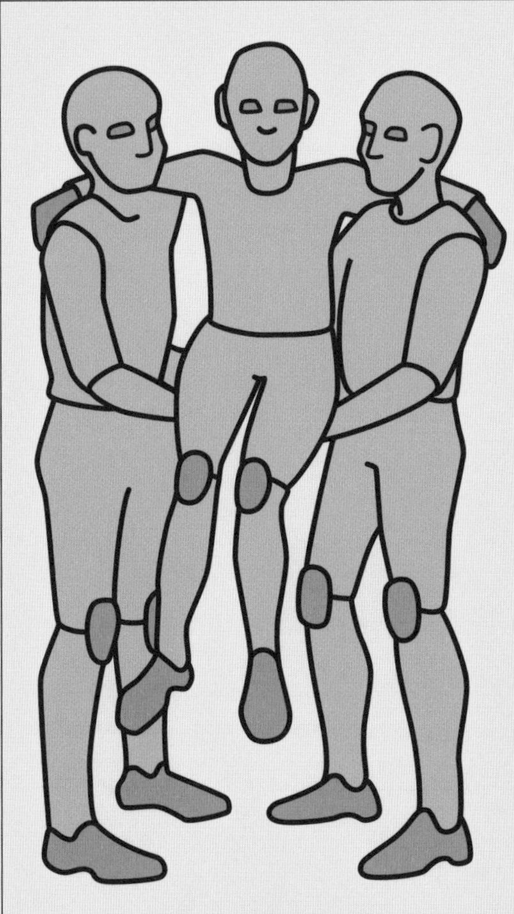

CARRY YOUR ADVENTURER

01. Position your injured adventurer on the stretcher.

02. Choose one of your team to be the lead. They will need to walk ahead of the stretcher to warn those carrying the stretcher of any dangers or difficult terrain.

03. Using as many people as you can, evenly space yourselves along the sides of the stretcher.

04. With bended knees grasp the stretcher and on the lead's command lift together in a smooth movement, remembering to keep your backs straight.

05. On the command from the lead begin carrying.

06. All commands from the lead must be followed in order to ensure safe passage for all parties.

We swung one of our ground cloths over a low-hanging branch and set out our makeshift camp for the night. Julian built a fire while George went for more water and Anne did her best to produce some lunch for us with our meagre supplies. By foraging for extra food in the woods (she found some wild hazelnuts and berries), Anne had us all fed and saved some food for our dinner later. It wasn't nearly enough to satisfy the Five's appetites, but we didn't complain.

Despite our run of bad luck and Dick's injury, we were in fairly good spirits. Camping and making do for ourselves always seemed the best of times for the Five.

"It's funny how our hols have taken us everywhere but where we planned to go, isn't it?" remarked George.

"Well, I think our side-adventure to the castle and camping in the woods were the best things to do under the circumstances," said Julian. "We found two important clues. We know that it was the navigator who wrecked the *Peregrine*; and we know that the letters EYT mean something. We'll get back on the trail soon, I'm sure. We'll go to St Agnes tomorrow and somehow we'll figure out the meaning of that map to the *Peregrine's* wreck, too."

Julian had a determined look in his eye that we all shared. We were all keen to get back to our mysterious adventure, even Timmy. We wanted to get back to tracking down Captain Kirrin's ship and the precious cargo it was carrying. We were determined to find the Royal Dragon of Siam.

The Diary of Julian Kirrin - Penzance

25th August, about 5 o'clock in the morning

Blast this run of bad luck! We should have been on St Agnes by now. As it is, we'll have only a few days to spend on the islands before having to return with Uncle Q on the 29th. We shall have to work very fast while we're there.

Well, I can't sleep, so I shall update my clues log until the others wake up. I must say, with the mystery of the Royal Dragon unfolding apace, this log helps me to keep all of our discoveries in the right order.

The Mystery of the Royal Dragon - Clues Log

Compiled by Julian Kirrin

CLUE DETAILS	DATE	SOURCE	MEANING?	ACTION?
Reporter mentions that Peregrine was wrecked somewhere off Land's End	16 Aug	Reporter Beverly Butlerton	Could there be treasure on board? (as there was on HJK's other wreck)	Dick keen to find out more. When and where did Peregrine go down? Check Uncle Q's library.
Peregrine sunk off Scilly Isles, late Oct 1859 – the Royal Charter Storm!	16 Aug	History of Maritime Disasters, Vol. III, 1850-1899	Wreck of Peregrine is somewhere in waters around Scilly	Can we find exact location? George to unearth HJK's old box of papers – could hold clues. **Box now given to Butlerton – but we have most interesting looking contents!**
There is a legend about treasure on board Peregrine!	17 Aug	Butlerton again	We have a new mystery on our hands!	The Five are agreed – we must find and search the wreck for the treasure!
Bags gone through and George 'kidnapped' on Penzance train	19 Aug		Someone trying to sabotage our trip? Why? Who?	Be vigilant! I don't trust Butlerton; think she had something to do with this . . .
Anne told Butlerton about our trip!	19 Aug	Anne Kirrin	Butlerton looks more and more the likely suspect for today's events	Don't tell others yet. Might be nothing? (Doubt it.)

CLUE DETAILS	DATE	SOURCE	MEANING?	ACTION?
Peregrine wreck no accident	20 Aug	HJK note and sketch	Traitor on board!	HJK writing to Duke – will name traitor.
Duke letter had coded message: 'send me a map to where the ship sank'	20 Aug	Anne cracked the code!	Our suspicions that the treasure is still in the wreck must be true. (Did HJK and Duke retrieve the treasure?)	We need to find the map that HJK sent to Duke. HOW???
HJK says traitor escaped the wreck – it was his navigator (no name given)	22 Aug	HJK letter to Duke, 16 Nov 1859	Why is it of the utmost importance for HJK to let the Duke know of the traitor's identity? Just so they can bring him to justice? Doesn't quite sound right . . .	
A strange piece of fabric with grid stitched on (26x3 boxes). Three boxes marked with knots.	22 Aug	Wrapped around HJK letter above	~~THIS MUST BE THE MAP! But it's coded. Possible meanings: a) knots symbolise islands around Scilly (wreck in centre?); b) one island is 26 x 3 yards? (treasure on island? NO! all evidence points to treasure being in wreck!)~~	George cracked it – the clue is letters! EYT. What do they mean? Not an island, that doesn't fit. These letters hold the clue for the Peregrine's whereabouts. Must discover what they mean!

After an uncomfortable night, we woke the next day and hurried to check on Dick's ankle. It was much better. There was no bruising and the swelling had all but gone. It was still a little tender so Julian found Dick a sturdy branch to use as a walking stick.

Anne quickly packed up our things and George put the last few bits into her own bag. Suddenly, George let out a great shout. The rest of us thought she'd found a snake in her bag and were terrified. We couldn't believe what she said next.

"The map! I've found the Captain's real map! It's here, inside this envelope. I don't know how we never spotted it before! I just looked down and there it was – staring me in the face!" With that, George pulled out one of the Captain's letters to the Duke and tore the envelope open carefully, spreading it flat so that we could see the inside.

And she was right! She had found the secret map!

Oh, the Captain had been very clever indeed. The map looked like nothing more than the backing design inside an expensive envelope. On it was a swirly map of the Scilly Isles with one island clearly marked to set it apart from the others. We could hardly believe it. While we were celebrating our change of fortune, Julian suddenly stopped short.

"But … if this is the map, and it quite clearly is, what, then, is that scrap of fabric about? What do the letters EYT mean?"

The rest of us simply didn't care about those letters at that moment. Finally, we knew exactly where the *Peregrine* sank! Hurrah! After our run of bad luck, we'd ended up with the very clue we'd been seeking all along. Our adventure was really taking off!

Tomorrow, we would be on the Isle of St Agnes and just a short boat ride away from uncovering the Royal Dragon!

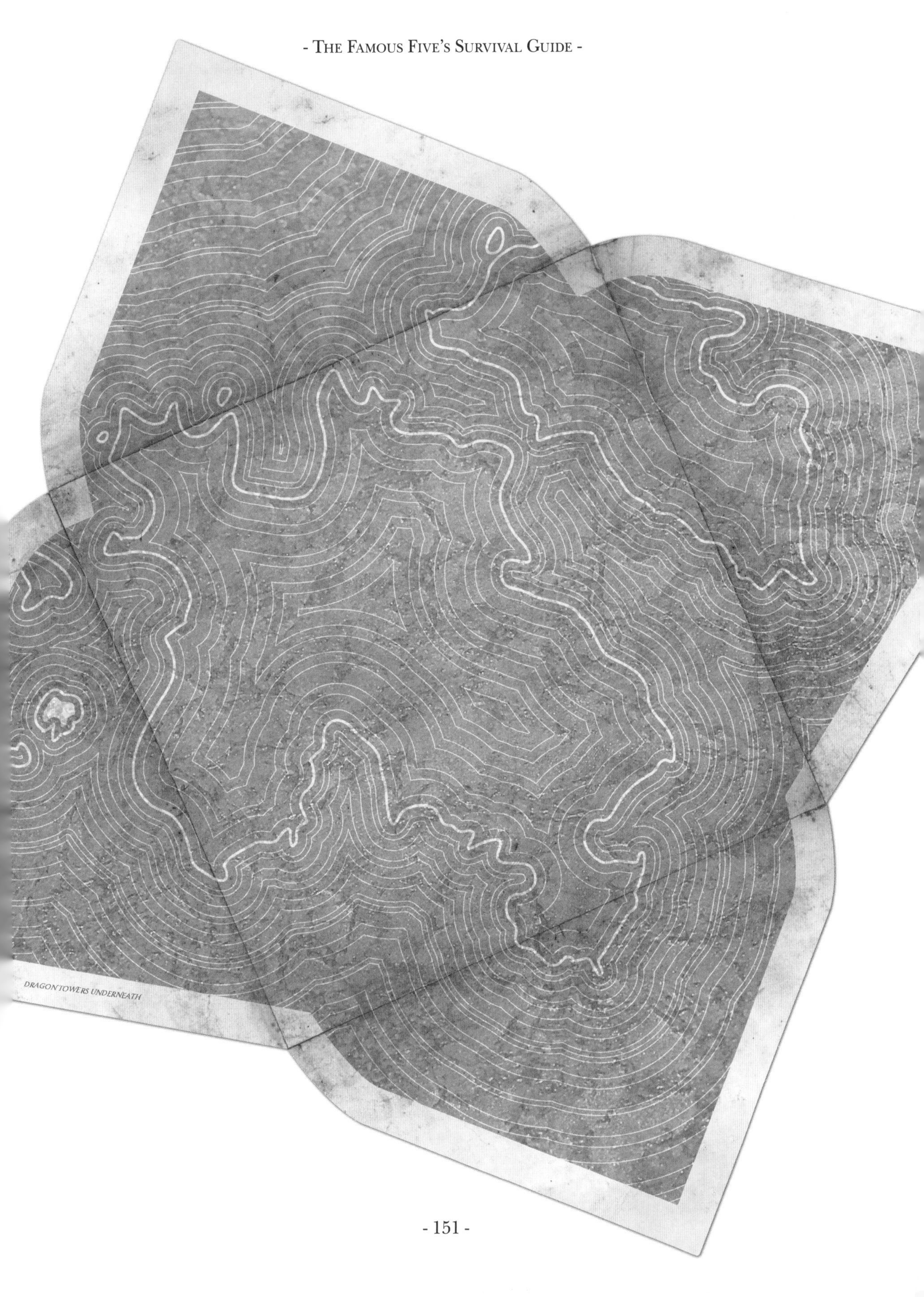
DRAGONTOWERS UNDERNEATH

Chapter Six

Important Discoveries

After three nights and three mishaps in the woods, we finally showed up, tired and muddy, on the Pollacks' doorstep. Mrs Pollack was very relieved to see us all in one piece.

"Thank goodness you children are all right!" she exclaimed. "You were supposed to be back days ago. I've been worried sick! I sent a couple of the local lads searching for you in the woods. But you weren't in the spot that Hugh recommended to you!"

We felt terrible for causing Mrs Pollack such a fright and were quick to explain what had kept us longer than we'd planned.

"You poor things!" she cried, instantly softening. "Well, at least your timing's good; I'm just about to take lunch in to your uncle and Mr Pollack. Go through, children, go through. You'll soon be tucking into thick tomato soup with bread and butter, a baked ham with crackling, roast potatoes, sweet carrots and fresh peas!"

We hadn't eaten properly in two days and the kindly Mrs Pollack had made all our mouths water. After we'd cleaned our faces and hands, we all indulged ourselves in the delicious food and still made room for thick slices of moist chocolate cake (which George shared with Timmy under the table while Uncle wasn't looking) with strawberries and lashings of cream.

Finally, all of us having sighed with satisfaction, Julian decided to broach the subject of our leaving almost immediately for St Agnes.

"Uncle, as we were unavoidably delayed in the woods, we'd rather like to set out to St Agnes today. With your permission, of course, Sir," said Julian in his most grown-up voice.

"You shall do nothing of the sort," announced Uncle Quentin. "We must return home in a few days. Your aunt called today especially to remind me that I must get you children home in plenty of time for the new school term on the 1st of September. You don't have time to go island hopping."

"Father!" cried George in alarm. Julian signalled to her that he would handle the situation but George would not be quieted. "We'll only stay a day or two," she argued. "We've come all this way to see the Scilly Isles, and now you say we must leave without seeing them! It's just not fair!"

"Georgina!" admonished Uncle Quentin (knowing how much George hates being called by her full name). "I trust you don't need reminding about your headmistress's warning that if you miss any more school, you shall be held back a year?"

Poor George hung her head in shame. It was true; George hadn't been applying herself at school and would need to put her good brain to better use in the coming year. (With plenty of help and encouragement from Anne, George did do that of course, and she wasn't held back a year.)

Uncle Quentin nodded. "I'll hear no more about it," he said with finality.

George scowled and the rest of us hung our heads in disappointment – even Timmy. We thought that our search for the Royal Dragon would have to be abandoned before it had really begun. But then Mr Pollack, who apparently didn't relish the idea of four noisy children and a rambunctious dog getting under his feet for the next four days, came to our aid.

"Let them go, Quentin," he advised. "A quiet house is just what we need to finish the crucial portion of our experiment. I can recommend a fine guesthouse on St Agnes. I know the owner personally and she will ensure that the children return in time for your train home."

With some further encouragement, Uncle Quentin finally agreed. "Very well. But I will meet you on St Agnes on the 29th to make sure we're in plenty of time for our train home. I shan't accept any excuses for lateness. I'm warning all of you – George especially!"

Julian spoke up immediately to reassure Uncle Quentin that we wouldn't be late, and the rest of us all promised the same. Mr Pollack went off to phone his friend at the guesthouse and Mrs Pollack offered to help the girls pack some more food for our journey.

Without further ado (and before Uncle could change his mind), we quickly refreshed our supplies and set out together again. On our way to the ferry, Julian told us that he'd identified the island Captain Kirrin had marked on his clever hidden map. By studying the shapes and positions of the islands, Ju was sure that the large one was St Agnes and that the small island marked by the Captain, near which he had lost his ship, was called 'Riddle Island'. We were thrilled with the name and couldn't wait to explore it! None of us spoke about the new school term looming next week. How can summer hols end so quickly?

Anne's Diary - 25th August, 1959

Richards' Guest House, St Agnes - Late evening

Well, Diary, we've finally made it to the Isles of Scilly! We're staying in a charming guesthouse run by Miss Richards. It sits on top of a high hill and from the room I'm sharing with George there is a spectacular view of the coast. Miss Richards strikes me as a calm and capable woman who is very good at looking after people – perfect for running a guesthouse. Julian and I were chatting to her earlier and we have already made some important discoveries . . .

I asked Miss Richards about the island I can see from the window of my room and was happily surprised to learn that it is Riddle Island – the very place where the Peregrine sank!

"Oh, you don't want to go there," said Miss Richards. "It's a craggy old island, that one – very harsh terrain. And nothing for you children to explore. Just an old water tower, that's all. I'm sure you'd much rather explore St Agnes itself."

Miss Richards went on to tell us that St Agnes has a fine maritime museum run by the Harbourmaster. It's full of information about clippers, captains and shipwrecks.

I gave a gasp of excitement at this and Julian shot me a warning look.

We told George and Dick about what we'd learned and they agreed that a visit to the maritime museum first thing tomorrow morning is an excellent idea. I do hope we can discover some more clues about the Peregrine. It is exciting to think we are finally close to uncovering the Royal Dragon of Siam!

I must say that Riddle Island looks rather rugged from my window. I wonder if the excitement of exploring it will be too much for me. I'm not very good at adventuring, Diary, as you know.

We arrived at the maritime museum early the next morning. It wasn't grand like some museums, and the Harbourmaster, Mr Rivers, didn't mind Timmy coming in at all. George took an immediate liking to Mr Rivers.

"Mr Rivers, sir, have you ever heard of the sinking of the *Peregrine*?" asked Julian. "She went down in the Royal Charter Storm of 1859."

"Hmmm, sounds familiar," replied the Harbourmaster. He went into his records room to pull out a file on the Royal Charter Storm. "Can't quite place it though. These islands were treacherous during those times. Scallywag wreckers used to lure ships to their death out on the jagged rocks."

Julian explained that the captain of the *Peregrine* was our great-great-great-grandfather and that we were interested in learning more about his ship. Mr Rivers turned back to us, carrying a large box. "Here's everything to do with the ships that went down during the time you're talking about," he said. "It was a wicked big blow, that Charter Storm, still talked about in these parts. Well, I've got things to do so I'll leave you kids to it. Just shout if you need anything."

As soon as we were alone, we dived into the pile of old papers and articles, looking for anything about the *Peregrine*. We were delighted with what we found that morning!

Luckily for us (and for you), Harbourmaster Rivers was something of a technology buff and had acquired one of the first 'xerography machines' created by a company called Xerox in 1959. With the help of this ingenious machine, we were able to take copies of the most interesting documents we found. We've enclosed them here for you.

Clipper Peregrine and her Crew, 25th October 1859.

Full Crew List of the Peregrine

25th October 1859

Kirrin, Henry J.	Captain
Turnbolte, Evan Y.	Navigator
Hannaway, Andrew M.	Steersman
Wilford, William S.	Conner
Longford, John J.	Pilot
Osborne, William M.	Surgeon
Caspell, William M.	Master Gunner
Teasdale, Edward C.	Gunner's mate
Yardley, William A.	Gunner's mate
Nobe, Thomas R.	Carpenter
Usher, James A.	Carpenter's mate
Manypenny, Richard N.	Boatswain
Matthews, Isaac G.	Boatswain's mate
Barnicoat, James E.	Cook
Cowling, Samuel L.	Quartermaster
Jones, Jake O.	Quartermaster
Saxelbye, James N.	Cooper
Digby, John A.	Swabber
Tricker, Edmund T.	Swabber
Elkington, Charles T.	Sailor
Thomas, David Y.	Sailor
Grovesnor, William M.	Foremast man
Knight, William P.	Foremast man

The St Agnes Weekly Report - November 28th, 1859

A WICKED STORM'S TERRORS AND TREASURES

The 'Royal Dragon of Siam' now lies in the heart of Scilly's own isles.

The body of sailor Jacob Jones was found washed ashore on Tuesday by St Agnes local Jill Beaverstock of Ilkley Road. Jones is the latest of the many victims who have washed ashore in the past weeks since the 'Royal Charter Storm', now estimated to have taken more than 500 lives. Jones was a quartermaster on Captain H.J. Kirrin's *Peregrine* out of Cardiff, which sank during the storm.

A SECRET CARGO

There is a surprising twist in the story of the *Peregrine*. This newspaper has learned that the ship was reportedly carrying a priceless treasure, the so-called 'Royal Dragon of Siam', a prized possession of the King of Siam himself.

The Dragon was stolen some weeks ago by international jewel thief Nathaniel Lunbertot. Its value on the black market is reputed to be one million pounds. Our source claims that the removal of the Dragon is the real cause behind the breakout of the civil war currently ravaging the Siamese kingdom. (*The St Agnes Weekly Report* is now investigating this outlandish claim.) Nathaniel Lunbertot seems to have disappeared. The jewel thief remains at large and continues to evade capture. Scotland Yard have no leads on his current whereabouts but have made Lunbertot's capture their number one priority.

However, the Royal Dragon of Siam has resurfaced. It was apparently brought to England and somehow intercepted by the honourable Duke of Dibeltoynn. The Duke arranged its return to Siam in order to bring an end to the civil war. Captain Kirrin's *Peregrine* was secretly returning the stolen royal treasure when it was wrecked.

Dear reader, that treasure - whose return could mean the end to a violent civil war - is now lost at the bottom of the sea!

Goodness! Our first glimpse of the Royal Dragon of Siam! We could hardly contain our excitement. Dick whistled and we were all chattering excitedly when Harbourmaster Rivers came back in.

"Glad you children are enjoying yourselves," he said, thankfully finding it perfectly natural that four children and a dog would be leaping about excitedly in the middle of a maritime museum.

"I came back to tell you that I remembered where I'd heard about the *Peregrine* before. A lady came in the other day asking about it. She was very demanding, so I did some digging about. I found this envelope with a seal at the top. Contents don't seem to have anything to do with the *Peregrine,* mind, but I think this is an original envelope. Would you like it? Didn't much like that lady. Found her rude. If you children want the envelope, I'll tell her I couldn't find anything."

Julian took the envelope from Mr Rivers. He gave the rest of us a meaningful look – no-one else would have noticed, but we recognized the excitement in his face immediately. For there, at the top of the envelope, unmistakably, was the same seal that was on the *Peregrine* Captain's Log!

"We'd be delighted to have it, thank you," said Julian. "Where did you get it, Mr Rivers?"

"I've no idea," replied the Harbourmaster. "People send things in that they pick up at jumble sales or find in their attics. The seas were very busy around these parts in Victorian times. People send me all sorts of things to do with shipping of that period, that's largely why I set up this museum."

We thanked Mr Rivers and waited for him to get back to his work. As soon as we were alone, we opened the envelope. Inside was a single piece of paper; another old newspaper clipping which told a very interesting piece of the Royal Dragon story. We've included it here for you.

TRAITOR! They can't have got far. Had to hide Dragon fast. They'll go back later. H.J.K

THE ST AGNES W

December 8th, 1859

JEWEL THIEF C

After months on the run and evading justice, Nathaniel V. Lunbertot has finally been arrested by constables for his rash of brazen jewel robberies that have terrorized international high society.

He was apprehended on the neighbouring island of St Ives and is being held for trial. Also arrested was the robber's accomplice, Edwin 'Spike' Spencer, a member of the lighthouse brigade and long-suspected leader of a gang of wreckers.

Readers may remember that Lunbertot is th scoundrel who stole the Royal Dragon of Siam (*St Agne Weekly Report*, 28th November). This priceless roya heirloom has been the subject of much speculatior Its disappearance is believed to have caused the Siames civil war. This newspaper can now confirm that story For the Royal Dragon of Siam is the stuff of legend ...

EEKLY REPORT

UGHT!

THE LEGEND OF THE ROYAL DRAGON

The Royal Dragon is said to hold the spark of fire reathed by the fiercest and most terrible beast.

Legend has it that long, long ago, when the first eople came to Siam, they were ruled by a menacing fire-reathing dragon. The Siamese people lived in fear for nany, many years. Despite the attempts of several valiant nen, no one could slay the dragon.

One day, a clever man tricked the dragon into eating ood filled with a sleeping draught. When the beast was ast asleep the clever man stole the dragon's spark, endering the dragon docile and powerless. rom that day forward, kings have ruled Siam, not errible beasts.

The clever man became the first King of Siam. He transformed the dragon spark into the star ruby and ad the ruby set into the precious Royal Dragon. A ejeweled dragon was forged, with the spark clenched in he Dragon's claw. For centuries, the Royal Dragon has een passed down from king to king, for he who holds he Royal Dragon becomes the rightful King of Siam.

With the Royal Dragon stolen away from Siam, no uling royal family had a claim to the throne. Rebel factions saw their chance and battled to seize ontrol of Siam in a cruel and bloody civil war. Only the afe return of the Royal Dragon will bring peace and rder back to Siam.

BROTHERS RETURN HOME SAFELY

With so many ships and brave souls lost in the recent storms, it is with great joy we bring you the news that local brothers Tobias and Harvey Bennett have returned home to their family and to a hero's welcome from the rest of the town.

When their ship the *Amelia-Jane* went down in the recent storm off the coast of Liverpool with the loss of many lives, the town feared the worst for the local characters. Well-known around St Agnes for their many hi-jinks which have seen them in trouble with the local police on more than one occasion, the brothers were feared lost by their family when no news had been received of the fate of their ship. But it seems the fates smiled upon these two brothers and returned them to their family.

The Bennetts also became heroes, rescuing five other of their shipmates from certain doom despite their own injuries, risking their lives to help with the rescue and salvage efforts on the stricken ship.

The brothers have been recovering from their injuries in Liverpool and their family were informed last week of their safety.

Despite their recent ordeal the brothers have vowed to return to the sea after they have spent some time with their family recuperating from their terrifying encounter with the forces of nature.

A memorial for those who perished on the *Amelia-Jane* will be held at the parish church during this Sunday's service led by Rev. Bickersnuff.

Astonished at what we had discovered, none of us could speak for several moments. We were thrilled by the legend of the Royal Dragon, but devastated by what Captain Kirrin's hand-scrawled note on the newspaper cutting implied. Finally, George broke the silence and voiced the thought that had gripped us all.

"He thought they'd hidden the Dragon? And that they'd go back for it later? But, that must mean that … the treasure isn't in the wreck of the *Peregrine* at all!"

Timmy laid his head on George's lap and looked up at her sympathetically. We were all bitterly disappointed.

"Blow!" cried Julian. "Our trip to the maritime museum has indeed led us to more information about the *Peregrine* and the Royal Dragon – but it's also dashed our hopes of uncovering the treasure ourselves!"

"It could be anywhere, couldn't it?" wailed Dick. "There's nowhere else that we can search for clues – we'll never find the Royal Dragon now!"

Just then, Anne cried out to us. "Wait! You must see this!" she called. Have you spotted what Anne did?

"Look," directed Anne, pointing to a sailor in the picture of the *Peregrine* crew and the thief in the newspaper article. "I think it's the same man!"

"It is indeed, Anne!" exclaimed Julian. "Even without the eye patch, I'd say the shape of the mouth and chin are identical. Lunbertot was aboard the *Peregrine*!"

"Now, there's a mystery," marvelled Dick, looking at the pictures.

"I'd say Lunbertot lied his way onto the *Peregrine* specifically to steal the Dragon back and claim his million pounds," figured Julian. "Is his name on the crew list?"

We examined the crew list for a Lunbertot but there was no mention of him.

We'd exhausted our search of the maritime museum and could think of nothing else to do but to make our dejected and downhearted way back to Miss Richards' guesthouse. But there was a surprise waiting for us, just around the corner …

The Diary of Julian Kirrin - St Agnes

26th August, evening

Our visit to the maritime museum filled in many of the missing pieces of our mystery. We found out that the Royal Dragon really exists and that a jewel thief aboard the Peregrine stole it. Where the treasure is now, perhaps we'll never know.

Yes, this day has been full of unpleasant surprises. On our way out, we ran straight into Reporter Butlerton, here on St Agnes!

I stopped to thank the Harbourmaster on my way out so I was too late to stop Anne from speaking to the reporter. Poor Anne, she is terribly bad at keeping a secret! She was in the middle of telling the reporter that the legend of a treasure aboard Captain Kirrin's ship was real! I think, though, that we learned more from the exchange than she did.

"Don't believe any of the stories you've heard about hidden treasure around here," jeered Butlerton. "None of them are true."

"But what about your own story about the Peregrine?" I interrupted.

She looked startled but quickly recovered. "Utter nonsense, I assure you. Honestly, can you imagine? A treasure map torn in two . . ."

She stopped abruptly, as if she'd said too much.

"A treasure map torn in two?" I asked. "Is that what you said?"

"You misunderstood ... I said, talk of a treasure map isn't true."

At that instant, Reporter Butlerton looked me straight in the eye as if she was trying to prove that she was telling the truth.

"Locals tell these stories to lure tourists to these islands. If you believe all you hear, then every sunken ship has the crown jewels aboard!"

All the while she was speaking, Butlerton was glancing nervously around her. I asked her if she was meeting someone.

"Oh, no. I'm not meeting anyone," she said. "I'm here all by myself."

Miss Butlerton's voice became rather squeaky, then, for no reason, she began to laugh. She quickly covered her mouth and stopped laughing just as suddenly. It was very odd behaviour indeed.

I brought the conversation to an end by claiming that we were late getting back for lunch. We said goodbye and all but ran away from the strange woman!

HOW TO SPOT A LIAR

What a tangled web we weave

Having finally cornered the slippery customer you've been trailing, he gives you some vital information that could crack the entire case. Do you trust what he has told you? How do you know if he's telling the truth?

GET SOME REFERENCE

01. Before you can tell whether anyone is lying, you are going to need a reference point for their normal conversational actions and body language.

02. Someone may exhibit all the usual signs of being a liar in their natural speech patterns. Ask the person you are talking to for some information that you know they will not lie about. You can then use their reactions as a gauge for when they are giving false details.

BODY LANGUAGE

A person can lie with their words, but their body movements will still give them away. Next time you're suspicious that someone is lying to you, watch their body movements, they'll tell the truth even if the person won't.

01. Liars try to avoid eye contact if they can. But be careful, expert liars will stare you straight in the eye to prove that they're NOT lying.

02. Those telling you a falsehood have a habit of looking all around them while spinning their yarns. They're looking for a way to escape their lies.

03. They tend to act nervous, tap their foot, twiddle their thumbs, touch and cover their mouth to hide their lies.

STRANGE BEHAVIOUR

It's not all about facial movements though, some liars exhibit other behaviour that is abnormal for them. Watch out for some of these signs.

01. Their laughter is loud and forced and their smiles are fake.

02. A liar won't face you. They often try to hold something between you and them, like a book, or papers.

03. Watch the person's eyes. If they are continually looking up to their right, before or as they answer, they are searching the right hand side of their brain for the answer. The right side of the brain controls the more creative side of the personality, hence they are searching for a creative answer, whereas by looking to the left they will be accessing the more factual side of their brain.

VOICE CLUES

01. A liar's voice will often break and stumble.

02. They mumble their words.

03. Their voice may suddenly go from normal to high-pitched squeaking and then back to normal.

04. Liars talk very fast. They don't want you to hear what they're saying.

WORD WATCH

01. One trick to look out for is if the person repeats your question right back to you.
"Do you have the treasure map?"
"No, I do not have the treasure map."

02. Liars will also avoid using contractions. For instance they'll say 'do not' instead of 'don't'. They think talking like this makes them sound serious and truthful.

03. Listen for too much information. Someone who was being truthful would have answered the above question by just saying 'No'. Liars tend to make up elaborate stories, especially when they don't have to.

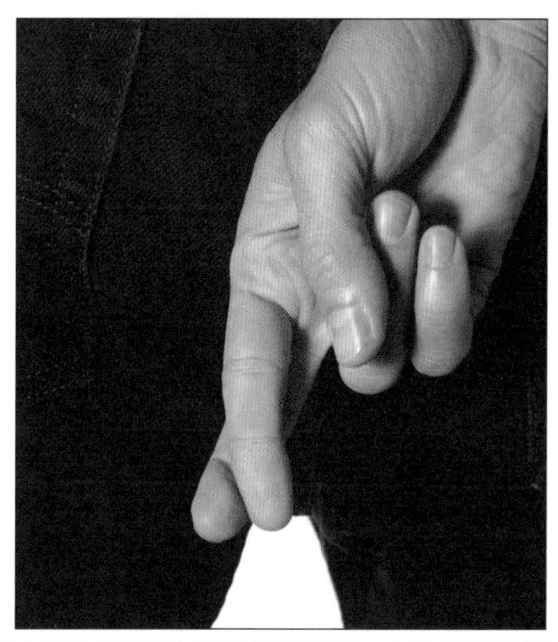

GET THE TRUTH

Interrogation skills

The purpose of an interrogation is to obtain information that an individual does not want to give. A successful interrogation is one where the interrogator recovers this information, but this is not always the case. On average ten per cent of subjects will not confess, or divulge information, even where the investigator is skilled and experienced. There are many reasons for this, and not all are within the investigator's control. However, there are certain things that the interrogator can practise which will help increase their chances of success.

INTERROGATION PREPARATION

Proper preparation is one of the most important factors in conducting a successful interrogation.

Location
The investigator must be in complete control; of the discussion, and the setting. It is important to ensure the environment is as conducive as possible to eliciting information. A small, private, space free of distractions such as clocks, windows and telephones will make the subject focus solely on the questions they are being asked.

Research
Knowing the subject's background and the case, or the circumstances around the information you are trying to retrieve, is possibly the most important factor in interrogation success. This research will allow the investigator to control the interrogation and to persuade the subjects that confessing is in their best interest.

GIVING PERSUASIVE ARGUMENTS

Certain words, phrases and concepts can help obtain a confession from a suspect. Knowing your

subject, their background, thoughts and feelings, can help the interrogator decide which method will elicit the best result.

Projecting blame

A good way to get your suspect to confess is to give them a chance to blame someone, or something, else. It allows them a get out clause and a way to rationalize their actions.

Rationalizing their actions

Rationalizing a suspect's actions by using phrases such as "anyone in that situation could have . . .", or "I understand how you might. . ." can give the suspect a dignified way to admit their involvement in something and to offer explanations for it. Rationalization offers suspects a chance to present their actions, or information, in a positive light.

Minimizing the crime

Making the crime, or the information you are trying to extract, seem less serious can increase the chances of your subject telling you what they know. Using words such as 'accident' and 'mistake' help reduce the gravity of the situation.

PROVIDE REASONS TO CONFESS

To increase the chances of your suspect confessing, after you have used persuasive arguments, give them reasons to confess.

Possible reasons

Encourage your suspect to believe that confessing will help them in some way. Knowing your subject thoroughly will help you know which line of suggestion will appeal to them. You will need to understand your subject's background and personal situation thoroughly to know what might motivate them.

For some suspects, releasing the burden of guilt or pressure they feel carrying their secret around could be reason to confess. Others might want some help, such as medical treatment. Or simply a chance to tell their side of the story may be enough for some subjects to tell their truth.

CREATE A RELATIONSHIP

It is vital to build a good relationship with a subject. Empathy is very important. A good interrogator will make their subject feel that they can see things from the subject's point of view. Sometimes an individual will give up the information they hold just out of admiration, respect and trust for their interrogator.

KNOW YOU WON'T ALWAYS SUCCEED

Knowing that even the most talented interrogators cannot crack every subject will stop you getting discouraged if your interrogation is not successful. Many hard-core criminals and repeat offenders are usually subjects of failed interrogations, even when the investigator has had years of training.

In order to help you succeed, ensure you have prepared thoroughly, perfected the arguments you intend to use and give your subject chances and reasons to confess. Properly addressing these factors will give you the best chance of interrogation success.

D.K. 26th August, 1959

Julian is snoring lightly but I can't sleep. Our visit to the Harbourmaster's proved to be quite informative. Maybe too informative. It's a bit of a muddle to sort out. I've been thinking and thinking about it, and I have some theories: The traitor Lunbertot was arrested several weeks after the Peregrine sank, so he must have safely got off the ship – probably stole a lifeboat, or something. Captain HJK believed that he had an accomplice, who had heartlessly lured the Peregrine to her dreadful fate on the jagged rocks of Riddle Island.

Now it turns out that HJK believed these rogues stole and hid the treasure somewhere close to where the Peregrine went down, intending to go back for it later. But who knows if it's still where they hid it all that time ago? Lunbertot, or his accomplice for that matter, could have gone back and taken the Dragon. Or HJK could have found it and sent it back to Siam. What a puzzle!

I talked to Julian about it, and he has his own theory on this point. The reporter mentioned a map torn in two. Julian thinks those scoundrels didn't even trust each other! He says they must have torn the map in half, so they'd have to come back for the treasure together. But where is it??

We're all feeling jolly rotten about the treasure not being in the wreck. We were all thoroughly convinced that we would find it there. But, since we've come all this way, we've agreed to visit Riddle Island tomorrow anyway and explore the Peregrine if we can. Mr Rivers can tell us how deep the waters are around the island – if they're not too deep, Ju says we should be able to dive down and explore for a few minutes at a time, just holding our breath. I do love looking over old ships!

Wait! Well, I never ... ! I think I've just realised what those peculiar initials EYT are all about! I must tell the others!

At the first sign of light the Five rushed downstairs and tucked into a hearty breakfast of porridge and fresh cream. We were excited about our trip to Riddle Island. Just because we couldn't find the Dragon, didn't mean we had to abandon all our holiday plans. If you want to be the best kind of child adventurer, you must always focus on the positive and approach each new day with energy and glee. And that's just what the Famous Five planned to do.

Dick came into the dining room virtually at a run. "I've discovered something I think might be rather important," he said, out of breath.

We all looked at Dick, waiting for him to explain.

"Those letters," he cried. "EYT. I've discovered what they mean!"

"I'd nearly forgotten about that clue!" said George.

"I hadn't," grumbled Julian. "I've been wondering about those letters myself. Well, be a sport, Dick. Don't keep us in suspense any longer."

"It's here in the *Peregrine* crew list. Look." Dick pointed to Evan Y. Turnbolte, Navigator. Of course! Julian remembered that Captain Kirrin had named his navigator as the traitor in one of his letters to the Duke – the clue had been staring us in the face all the time!

"That must be the name of the sailor with the eye patch!" said an astonished George. "The fellow we spotted in the *Peregrine* crew photo who turned out to be the jewel thief."

We all agreed that George was right. Then Julian let out an excited cry.

"I've got it! Turnbolte and Lunbertot!" he said. "They're anagrams of each other! Two different names spelled with the exact same letters."

Well! Julian was absolutely right, of course. We all thought he and Dick were awfully clever. At least we had managed to solve one of the many puzzles surrounding the mystery of the Royal Dragon. It put us into a fine mood as we collected our picnic basket from Miss Richards and headed out to St Agnes harbour, where we would borrow a boat from Mr Rivers for our trip to Riddle Island.

We could hardly wait for our visit to the deserted island, just the Five together. How thrilling!

Chapter Seven

The Treasure Room

From the desk of Georg~~ina~~e Kirrin

August 27th, 1959
Just arrived on Riddle Island

When we arrived at the harbour, Mr Rivers was happy to see us and already had a small sailboat waiting.

"Who's the captain here?" he asked.

Julian told him that I would be the captain on our excursion. I didn't want to brag, but I am the best sailor among us!

I showed Mr Rivers all I know about the sails and ropes and things. He was impressed, I think.

"Well, she'll be in good hands. I see that now!" he said, and then slapped me on the back! I do believe he's mistaken me for a boy! Isn't that grand? I knew he was a good sort the moment I saw him. Timmy likes him too, of course.

While the others stored our gear on the sailboat, I talked over the tides and currents that we would encounter on our sail to Riddle Island with Mr Rivers.

We haven't brought much gear as we only plan to spend a night out here. We need to get back to St Agnes tomorrow evening and Father will collect us the following morning. THE 29TH! Lest I forget ... What a bore it'll be to be back at school in a few days' time. I'd much rather sail about and visit all the islands around here! Even without a treasure to hunt for.

When we had all climbed aboard the Island Drifter, that's the name of our sailboat, I ran through our safety check.

George told us lots of seafaring lore that she learned from the fishermen around Kirrin Island. We've included it here for you, too. If you want to skip ahead and find out what was in store for us on Riddle Island, turn to page 176.

KEEP EVERYTHING SHIP-SHAPE

Before any novice sailor takes to the water there are a few things to bear in mind to ensure you return to your home port safe and sound

BEFORE YOU LEAVE

- **Know how to swim** – It's no good setting off in a boat if you feel uncomfortable in the water. Sailboats tip over - it's an unavoidable fact - and depending on the size of the craft, some tip more than others. The last thing you want at the end of your trip is to be coughing and spluttering half the local water source up from your lungs.

- **Never sail alone** – This doesn't mean you have to have a partner in your boat for every trip, but it's only common sense to at least have other people around to help in case of trouble.

- **Get a weather forecast** – Never leave port without knowing what the weather may be bringing you. Get your forecast from a reputable source, preferably a marine forecast, but don't just rely on the forecast. Keep your eye on the weather once you are out as things can change very quickly and without warning.

- **Carry lifejackets** – Make sure they are easily accessible. Don't just throw them in the boat and forget about them either - WEAR THEM!

- **Tell someone** – Before you leave port tell someone where you are going and when you plan to be back. Make sure you let them know when you return safely to port.

SAFE SAILING

If you need help don't be afraid to signal for it: other sailors and the Coast Guard will help but only if they are alerted. If you don't have a radio on board to call for help there are a number of other ways you can let passing ships know you are in distress.

International Distress Flag
Make sure you have one of these internationally recognized flags on-board every time you set out. The orange flag with a black circle and square emblazoned on it gives the benefit of excellent long-distance visibility that does not apply to many other forms of signal.

Smoke Them Out
During daytime hours another recognized way of signalling for help over distances while on the water is to release orange smoke, from either floating or handheld flares.

Wave for Safety
Stand on deck and slowly raise and lower your arms from your sides to above your head. Any passing ships will recognize this as a distress signal and not simply someone waving for the fun of it.

Flagless
If you don't have an international distress flag, another way of signalling for help is to attach a piece of clothing to an oar and hold it in the air.

CHECK AND BE SAFE

Check your deck before you leave to make sure you have everything you need for not only an enjoyable trip, but also for safety.

- **Life jackets**
  Must have these!
- **Radio**
  For up to date weather reports.

- **Mirror/Flashlight**
  For signalling during the day or night.

- **Compass**
  Never leave port without one.
- **Plastic tarp**
  For staying dry in heavy rains.

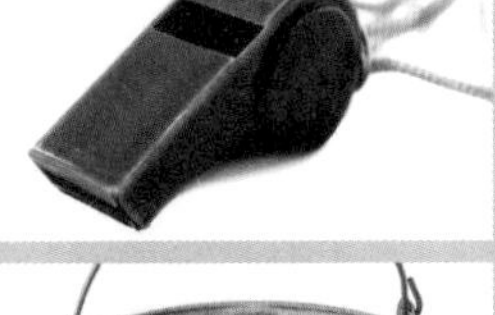

- **Whistle**
  For signalling for help.

- **Bucket**
  For bailing out the boat.

- **Oars**
  Just in case...
- **Emergency distress flag**
  Don't leave port without one.

- **Flares**
  For signalling other vessels.

- **Emergency food supplies**
  Ensure they are in a waterproof container.

GETTING YOUR WATER WINGS WET

A guide for the new sailor

This may be the first time you've taken to the water in a craft of your own, or you may well be an old sea dog who believes he has salt water running in his veins. Either way, knowing the basics of safe navigation is crucial – whether you plan to sail to the four corners of the Earth or simply enjoy a punt on your local lake on a Sunday afternoon.

RULES OF THE ROAD

To help keep everyone safe from collisions and accidents some basic rules must be followed when on the water. Think of it as a highway code for the water and make sure you follow the rules at all times. More detailed rules can be obtained from your local coastguard or sailing association and it is highly recommended you obtain a copy before taking to the water.

- Rowboats generally have right of way over sail and power boats.
- Sail boats generally have right of way over power boats.
- When two vessels approach each other, the vessel with the right of way is known as the 'stand-on' vessel, while the vessel giving way is known as the 'burdened' vessel.
- The person in control of the 'burdened' vessel has a duty to do everything possible to allow safe passage of the 'stand-on' vessel.
- When two sail-powered boats approach each other both with the wind on the same side, the leeward vessel (i.e. the one further downwind) shall have right of way.
- When two boats approach with the wind on differing sides, the vessel with the wind on their starboard side has right of way.
- Each boat has a 'danger zone'. Think of the bow as being 12 o'clock and the danger zone extends from 12 round to 4. You must give way to any craft in your danger zone.
- When meeting another craft head-on keep as far starboard as possible and allow the craft to pass along your port side.
- When overtaking, the vessel being passed is the privileged craft and overtaking may only commence when the privileged craft has been signalled and has agreed.

HAVE YOU JIBBED AND LUFFED PROPERLY?

Of course sailing has a language all its own. Make sure you don't look like too much of a landlubber by learning these basics.

- **Port** – Left side of boat (when facing towards bow).
- **Starboard** – Right side of boat (when facing towards bow).
- **Bow** – Front of boat.
- **Stern** – Rear of boat.
- **In Irons** – Stuck with the bow heading directly into the wind.
- **Jib** – Turning the stern of the boat through the eye of the wind.
- **Leech** – The back edge of the sail.
- **Leeward** – Side of the boat that is away from the wind.
- **Luffing** – Flag-like shaking/flapping of sail when not properly trimmed to catch the wind.
- **Run** – Sailing with the wind at the stern.
- **Tack** – Turning the bow of the boat through the eye of the wind.
- **Telltales** – Pieces of light material fastened to stays to aid in reading the direction of the wind.
- **Windward** – Side of the boat that is facing the wind.

George masterfully sailed the *Island Drifter.* Her hand never left the boat's tiller, as she instructed Julian and Dick to raise and lower the sails in order to catch the shifting winds. Anne and Timmy stayed in the bow out of the way of the swinging boom and sails. Even before we could see Riddle Island, George knew land was near. She could tell from the different ocean and sky signs. George has the keenest eyesight of the Five and spotted land a few minutes before the rest of us.

We dragged the sailboat up on to the sand and tied it to a stout tree. Looking about us, we realized that Miss Richards had been right about Riddle Island. It really was a 'harsh' and 'craggy' place. A rough and rocky hill stretched out behind us, high and imposing. On its top was the only structure on the island, an old, round tower.

"That's a Martello tower," said Julian quickly. "They're small defensive forts, built by the British Army from the time of the Napoleonic Wars onwards. A garrison of men would be stationed in one of those and it would be their job to protect the British Empire. Martellos are very resistant to cannon fire, you see. And because they're circular, one is able to see all the way around for any enemy that might approach. They're preserved now as historic monuments, you know. I can't imagine this one gets visited much, on this lonely island."

Even today, the rest of us marvel at the trivia Julian is capable of lodging in his brain. He was always just one of those people that knows something about simply everything – and insists on sharing it with those around him!

Dick teased him for being a boring old goat, which made us all laugh as we made our camp quickly on the beach and dived into the sea for a swim. Mr Rivers had told us we had no hope of finding the *Peregrine* as the water was very deep and full of large, jagged rocks. Nonetheless, George and Dick were determined to outdo each other, holding their breath under water and swimming as far down as they dared. Although there were many claims that one or the other had seen a mast or prow, we didn't get a glimpse of the *Peregrine.*

Julian didn't join us in the water, instead he pored over all the papers we'd collected about the mystery of the Royal Dragon. He wanted to make sure that we hadn't missed a clue. Do you know, it turned out that we had ...

The Diary of Julian Kirrin - Riddle Island

27th August, afternoon

I have found an important clue! One that I cannot believe I didn't spot before. I was going over all the papers and things we've collected to do with this mystery, hoping to find something new, and there it was. It was well hidden, of course.

It's inside the envelope that secretly shows the Isles of Scilly map. In the corner, in tiny handwriting is written: 'Dragon towers underneath'. It's almost too small to be sure, but I think the writing is Captain Kirrin's. This is surely an important clue – Captain Kirrin was telling the Duke of Dibeltoynn something about the treasure. What a puzzling message! Our ancestor was certainly a gifted puzzler because I have no idea what it could possibly mean. How can something tower from underneath? Unless it's an iceberg . . . ? It makes no sense!

When Julian showed us this overlooked clue, we were all stumped. We couldn't work out what it meant, and neither could we stop worrying over it in our minds. The mystery of the Royal Dragon had gripped the Five and with a new found clue, we were all enthralled by it once again. When one is in the middle of a complicated mystery like this one, it is sometimes difficult to put all the right clues together. We were lucky that Anne had such a good brain for puzzling things out. Read her diary to see what happened next ...

Anne's Diary - 27th August, 1959

Riddle Island, Famous Five beach camp.

Dear Diary,

I think I know where the treasure is. But I want to write it out here before I tell the others, just in case I am wrong. It's not that I mind looking silly (as you know, Diary, I've done that often enough before and my brothers and George never think badly of me for it – thank goodness!), it's rather that I don't want to give them false hope. We've had so many ups and downs on the trail of the Dragon already; it would be unfair to ignite our excitement again if I've gone and got my foolish brain in a spin over this latest clue.

Right. Let me see if this makes sense.

Our great-great-great-grandfather thought that the horrid Mr Lunbertot and his accomplice must have hidden the Dragon somewhere close to where the Peregrine sank. Then, surely it's feasible that they hid it on the very island we are camping on? And that cryptic clue he left on the map that he sent to the Duke – 'Dragon towers underneath'. That could mean that the Dragon is underneath the Martello tower here on Riddle Island. Couldn't it? I do believe it could . . .

Heavens! I'll tell the others!

"We must search the tower!" cried George, jumping up at Anne's news. Before we others could respond, she was already pulling her shoes and socks on, ready to make her way up the rocky hill to the Martello tower on top.

"Hang on, George," called Julian. "That hill will be tricky to climb. Let me think what the best way will be. We have some ropes with us, but I didn't bring any karabiners with me. Did you, Dick? I didn't think we'd be doing any rock-climbing on this holiday, I must say."

Anne immediately looked terrified at this news, while George looked positively delighted at the thought.

Julian and Dick quickly searched their gear for the D-shaped rings that mountaineers use when they are climbing. They hadn't brought any. Julian made us wait while he examined the face of the hill, planning which route would be easiest and quickest to the Martello tower. After a while, Julian decided that it would be safe for us to climb up, and that Dick would help Anne find her footing. We gathered up some essential gear (torches, trowels for digging, and our water canteens), and trekked to the foot of the hill.

Anne was obviously scared about attempting the climb, but having cracked the clue herself, she didn't want to be the only one not to explore the tower for the Dragon.

In just a few short minutes, the Five were ready to climb.

WARNING

Before beginning any rock climbing activity a solid set of safety plans is vital. This not only applies to your equipment but also to those who may be climbing with you. Rock climbing offers a fun and exciting sport that will keep you healthy and active, but should only be attempted with a qualified climber or guide accompanying you. Remember to get professional training, rock climbing can be dangerous and should only be attempted with the right training, gear and an experienced guide.

REACH THE HEIGHTS

Getting to grips with climbing

There's nothing to beat standing on the top of a crag admiring the landscape stretching before you, and knowing you've just conquered it yourself. Before you can reach this point though there are a few basics that you will need to know. It's not just a case of turning up at a rock and climbing it, although with the proper training it can be just that simple. As a taster of the sport we're giving you a few basic pointers. Don't worry, you won't be expected to climb K2 after this, but it should help to point you in the right direction.

EQUIPMENT

If you really want to get into climbing properly there are a number of routes you can take. From Bouldering (climbing large boulders without equipment) to full on Traditional (all the gear and usually huge rock faces), there are many levels at which to get into the sport and of course many levels of equipment that go along with it. How advanced you get is up to you. Essential for all types and levels of climbing though are some basic items of safety equipment.

HELMET

Probably the most important part of any rock climber's kit, whatever level they climb at, is a sturdy and solid helmet. This will protect you from possible falls, as well as any debris falling from above that could cause you harm. Make sure the helmet you purchase fits properly with no sign of wobble when adjusted to your head. Also make sure it is comfortable to wear and gives you plenty of head movement as visibility is vital when climbing.

SHOES

There are as many different shoes as there are snowflakes and it may well take a while before you find a shoe that you are comfortable with. Make sure you shop around as a good pair of climbing shoes can make a huge difference to your climb. Visit a professional climbing store and discuss your needs with the salesperson. Be sure to explain that you are a beginner climber.

HARNESS

Choosing the right harness will depend on the type of climbing that you will be doing. Traditional climbers look for a more solid harness, which they can attach all their equipment to, while the sports climbers look for something a little lighter. If you are not sure what sort of climbing you prefer as a starter it's best to go for something in the middle that offers both lightweight and comfort but also plenty of expansion options should the need arise.

ROPES

A whole array of ropes of varying lengths, thicknesses, ratings and weatherproofing are used in the sport of rock climbing and the many deciding factors on which you choose will depend on the rocks you are climbing. Make sure you get professional advice from a fully trained instructor before purchasing your own ropes.

TIPS FROM TOP CLIMBERS

- Rock climbing not only gives a great sense of achievement but also offers an excellent way to get fit as well as build strength and confidence.
- Climbing takes a real toll on the joints and muscles so make sure you warm up well before attempting a climb. You don't want to get a painful cramp in your leg while reaching for a foothold just because you didn't warm up properly.
- Before climbing any face, ensure you are aware of your climbing partners' abilities and have practised all the necessary skills required before setting off. Halfway up the side of a cliff is not where you want to learn a complicated new skill for the first time.
- Your first climbs will be as a follow-up climber attached to a more experienced climber. This does not mean you will never lead but it is an excellent place to hone your skills while the lead climber takes on the difficult task of marking a path for you to follow.
- Before starting your climb, visualize the route you will be taking up the face. Look at the rock from different angles from ground level. Trying to spot potential hand and foot holds will make things a lot quicker when on the rock itself.
- Use only the tips of your toes to place on grips. Many beginners make the mistake of placing their instep on the foothold. This will block your hips from twisting and make your next move a lot more difficult.
- Pay close attention to where you place your feet. While it is tempting to look elsewhere (for your next hand grip, for example), it's important to watch your foot all the way to its destination until it and you are stable.

TRAINING

There are lots of training options available with many gyms now offering climbing walls on which to practise your skills in safety and comfort during the winter months before tackling the real thing.

For more details of climbing sites, training schools and instructors, equipment suppliers etc. contact your local climbing centre or national organization.

UNITED KINGDOM

The British Mountaineering Council:
www.thebmc.co.uk

NORTH AMERICA

The American Alpine Club:
www.amercianalpineclub.org

AUSTRALIA

Sport Climbing Australia:
www.sportclimbingaustralia.org.au/

WORLDWIDE

International Mountaineering and Climbing Federation http://www.theuiaa.org/

Julian led the way, carefully planning the next spot to place his hands and feet, and calling directions back to Dick and Anne, who followed behind. George and Timmy brought up the rear, both of them comfortably scrambling over the rocks, just like a pair of confident mountain goats!

The closer we got to the tower, the more our anticipation grew. To think, that we were finally in the spot where the Dragon could be hidden! Dick was almost beside himself with excitement – already planning the commendations we'd receive from the King of Siam when we returned the ancient heirloom to its rightful owner!

Eventually we reached the top of the flat hill and stood side by side, looking at the Martello tower. We all felt rather daunted by the sheer size and loneliness of it. This desolate fortress certainly made a great hiding spot for a stolen treasure. Timmy didn't like the look of it one bit, whimpering softly to George as if to warn us against going in. But, naturally, we were determined that we would go in.

The entrance was high above ground level, and the stairs leading up to it were worn and rickety. As we carefully climbed them, Dick wondered out loud whether they'd support the weight of a fully-grown adult. (You see, sometimes it helps to be small when you're adventuring.)

The door was heavy and stiff; it took the five of us pushing together with all our might to get it open. Finally, we were able to step inside …

That old Martello tower was a terribly interesting building. If we hadn't been so focused on searching for the Royal Dragon, we could have spent the rest of the day exploring the fortress. As it was, our attention was immediately drawn to the two large holes in the tower floor. If Anne's reading of the clue was correct, one of these holes would surely lead us to the treasure!

The boys each knelt beside one of the holes, peering down into the dense darkness. We all had torches with us, and shone two into each hole. We were dismayed to see that the sturdy wooden staircases, that had once been used to climb down into the cisterns, had both been chopped away, with just their top rungs remaining.

"How are we to get down there now?" wailed Anne.

"We shall use our ropes, of course," said George. "Won't we Julian?"

We all looked to Julian for the final decision. "Yes, we will," he said firmly. "Dick, you and George search the hole on the right, while Anne and I search the one on the left." Timmy barked loudly, clearly unhappy about not having been assigned to search a hole. George chuckled and patted him. "You'll come with Dick and me, Timmy. Don't worry. We wouldn't leave you up here on your own, old boy."

Julian tested the strength of the remaining ladder rungs at the mouth of each hole, then decided that he would do better to attach our ropes to the huge pillar in the centre of the tower instead. Julian expertly tied our four ropes around the central pillar, and dropped two down into each hole. (When you're an adventurer, it's always best to carry LONG lengths of rope with you. That way you'll avoid the shameful situation of finding that your rope is too short for your requirements.)

George wrapped her jumper around Timmy's middle, and then tied one of the ropes around our brave and loyal friend. Together, Julian and Dick carefully lowered Tim down into the hole on the right. That hole was clearly very deep as we all felt that this took an interminable length of time. Finally, Timmy's sharp bark echoed out to us, signalling that he had finally reached his destination.

George grabbed the other rope and without a moment's hesitation, followed Timmy into the hole, her torch in one hand. She let out a delighted laugh. "Gosh!" she called up to us. "I can't quite see the bottom yet. Isn't abseiling fun?"

Anne's Diary - 27th August, 1959

Back at camp on Riddle Island.

Oh! Diary, I can't say how glad I am to be out of that dreary tower and back on this bright, if barren, beach. The hole that Julian and I had to search was the old water cistern and we both got soaked through! Darling Julian would have had me wait above while he searched the cistern alone, but I felt awfully cowardly up there while all the rest were busy searching so, in the end, I took a deep breath and lowered myself in. The water was freezing and I didn't dare imagine all the horrid things that might be living in it after all this time!

The hole was large but the water only came up to our knees so it was fairly easy to squat down and search the bottom. We ran our hands all along the inside of the water cistern and finally agreed that there was no secret nook or cranny where the Dragon might be hidden. Julian pulled himself out and then helped me out. We bent over the other hole and called to George and Dick. We got no answer and called again, more loudly, but could only hear the echo of our own voices coming back at us.

We were both wet and cold (for although it is late summer and warm out here, the inside of that bleak old tower is quite cool), but decided to go in after them straight away. Julian made sure that I stayed a good way behind him and held tightly to the rope. He wanted to make sure that if we ran into a sudden drop, I wouldn't fall and get hurt. I must say, if I hadn't been concerned for the safety of my brother and cousin, nothing would have got me to climb down such a long way with just that rope to support me! As it was, I was too worried about them to worry about the climb – it seemed over in no time. Julian says I was a real brick and that does make me proud!

We dropped down to find ourselves in a very small room with a narrow walkway off one end. George and Dick must have gone that way, so I followed Julian towards it, grateful for the light of our torches. The further we moved from the shaft behind us, the darker the tunnel became. We proceeded a few more yards and came into a wide-open room with a low ceiling and a hard-packed dirt floor, with walls made entirely of small bricks – not a window in sight. There were George, Dick and Timmy, smiling at us.

"This has to be where the Royal Dragon is hidden," cried Dick excitedly.

"We've named it the Treasure Room!" exclaimed George.

Even in our sorry state, Julian and I were immediately caught by their excitement. We could only conclude that they were right and that the Royal Dragon was hidden right there under our feet!

Oh! But what a frustrating time we've had since that moment!

D.K. 27th August, 1959

Thanks to Anne's cleverness today, we have found the Treasure Room! It simply MUST be the place where the Dragon is hidden. I'm sorry to say that we've searched the entire day but found nothing. All we have to show for our troubles are bruises and scrapes. I forgot my gloves and the ropes have given me quite a nasty burn.

Julian had us divide the floor into organized sections so we each dug into one corner of the room. We weren't sure what we were looking for – perhaps a tin box, or perhaps the Royal Dragon was in a pouch of some sort. I wasn't digging long before I came across a large, flat, round stone.

Our determined digging uncovered nothing else – not even a small pebble. I wondered whether the stone could be a marker, marking the place where the Dragon was hidden. Well, the others agreed with me but I must have been wrong because we dug that corner until both Ju and I were standing inside a hole that was almost as tall as we are. No Dragon. No sign of anything, in fact. The earth changed and became much harder, so we seriously doubt that the treasure could be hidden any deeper than that. While we concentrated on that corner, the girls (with Timmy helping!) dug a little way down into the other corners and also found nothing. Blow!

Poor Anne, she started to worry that she'd misunderstood those clues and had sent us on a wild goose chase. But, I can't help but wonder whether Butlerton's story of a treasure map is true. I feel there is something in that room that we are missing – we only need a map to unlock the secret. Something that explains what that marker was doing buried in the ground.

Blast! It really is too cruel, the way our hopes keep being lifted one moment and then dashed the next. Here we are, in reach of the Royal Dragon but without a map, we shall never find it! And there isn't any more time to waste. We must return to St Agnes tomorrow evening. We need a map!

Anne and Dick's diary pages from that day perfectly capture our fruitless adventure into the Treasure Room. We dug and dug every inch of the floor, all of us growing more and more frustrated. None of us wanted to give up the search.

We were so focused on searching for the treasure that we even forgot about lunch – something the Famous Five never did! That day, we worked right through it until we were all hungry and deflated.

After some coaxing from Anne, who was always the first of us to be worn out, we agreed to go back to our camp for a hearty lunch and a well-earned rest. We left the Martello tower; dirty, tired, and unable to hide our disappointment.

Dick was right. Finding the Royal Dragon without a map (if indeed Butlerton was telling the truth and there was a map) would be impossible.

As luck would have it, Timmy was about to take our search for the Dragon into his own hands, or rather his own paws. We'll let George's diary entry from that day explain …

From the desk of Georg~~ina~~e Kirrin

August 27th, 1959
Riddle Island beach

Good old Timmy! He is without a doubt the best dog in the world! But today, I must say, Timmy rather outdid himself.

We were sitting on the beach, tired out and frustrated at not having found the Dragon in that horrid tower on the hill, when Tim took up Dick's hat between his teeth and ran off with it. Timmy rather enjoys this game of chase and, as the others were so glum, I was happy to indulge him by running after him. When I caught up with Tim, I saw that he no longer had Dick's hat in his mouth. Instead, Timmy was holding an old leather boot between his teeth. The boot was tall and black and looked hundreds of years old – like the kind sailors used to wear in old pirate days.

"Timmy!" I shouted. "Drop that foul looking boot!" But he wouldn't. Instead he proudly stepped over to me with his head high, and presented the boot to me like a present.

"Timothy!" I cried, disgusted. "I don't want this dirty old thing. Drop it, I say!" Timmy only nudged the boot at me all the harder and wouldn't let it go until I took it from him.

It really is filthy! I suppose it was black once but it's almost white with salt and age now. There are some letters embossed onto the inside of the top part. S.S. Well, I thought the others might find it amusing to see what Timmy had found, so I took it back to camp to show them.

My goodness me! I can hardly believe what that dirty old rotten boot contained. Dick made to try it on for a joke and felt something lodged inside the foot. He stuck his hand in and pulled out a tube! The lid was rusted on tight, but Dick pried it open with his camp knife.

When we looked inside the tube, we couldn't believe our eyes. There was a rolled up piece of parchment inside, torn along one edge. Julian carefully unrolled the parchment and we finally saw what Timmy had found.
It is undoubtedly a sketch of the Treasure Room. Good old Timmy has found us a map!

We had found a map! Or at least we had found a sketch of the Treasure Room with some bemusing symbols on it. We had no idea what they meant. In fact, the 'map' raised more questions than it answered. Who was S.S.? Why had he hidden this map in his boot and apparently flung it away on Riddle Island? Did S.S. have a connection to the *Peregrine* or the Royal Dragon of Siam? And, most importantly, how could we find out?

Julian felt that we had come across these initials recently. Pacing back and forth through camp, he mumbled and pondered to himself about where he remembered seeing them. He had us check the *Peregrine* crew list again. We scanned it twice but there was no listing for anyone with the initials S.S.

We others wanted to help him but, really, his memory is so much better than ours that we felt if he couldn't remember, we certainly wouldn't.

George was impatient to get back to the Treasure Room so that we could use the cryptic map to help us find the Royal Dragon, but Julian was determined to solve the puzzle surrounding the initials and that boot. He knew that the answer was somewhere in the papers we'd collected. We all helped him search. Eventually, Julian let out a cry and we knew that he had found it.

"Aha!" he shouted. "It's here, in the news clipping about the jewel thief! I knew I remembered those unusual initials. Look here."

We looked and saw that the article mentioned a man named Edwin 'Spike' Spencer who had been arrested along with Lunbertot. Spike Spencer – S.S. and the article said that he was a wrecker!

"He must have been the wrecker on the Royal Dragon heist!" cried George. "The one who gave Captain Kirrin the guide light that sent the *Peregrine* crashing into these jagged rocks!" George indicated the treacherous sea around Riddle Island.

"Yes!" joined Dick. "And he hid his half of the map in his boot!"

"But, the map doesn't look like it's missing a half," mused Anne. "The sketch of the Treasure Room looks complete to me. Although, this parchment has obviously been torn off. I wonder what the other half of the map showed?"

"That's a mystery I don't think we can solve, Anne," said Julian. "But I'll bet that Lunbertot had the other half. No matter, we have half the map to the Royal Dragon of Siam! Tomorrow morning, we shall go back to the Treasure Room and see if these symbols make any sense to us."

Early the next morning, after a hurried breakfast, we grabbed our gear and headed back to the Treasure Room. We discussed whether to take a packed lunch with us to avoid the hunger we'd experienced yesterday but, in the end, we agreed that we would come back to camp for our lunch. Anne really didn't want to eat inside that dreary, confined little room. Taking only our water canteens, we set off again up the hill, to the hidden room beneath the Martello tower.

The day was the 28th of August, 1959, and we were under strict instructions to meet Uncle Quentin on St Agnes early the next morning, so we had to leave Riddle Island that day. George said that we'd need to leave well before sundown so as to avoid sailing at night in the treacherous waters. None of us mentioned that the very next day, we would have to leave the Scilly Isles and return to Kirrin – we really didn't want to think about having to abandon our search and begin a new year at school!

When we returned to the Treasure Room, we sat together in the centre of the floor, trying to make sense of the symbols on the map. We were fairly certain that the symbols showed the sun rising and setting, and the new and full moons. But what did they mean? Of course, we were most enthralled by the X in the corner. Did X mark the spot? We thought about this for a long time. Finally, we decided that in the mystery of the Royal Dragon, X marked the spot where we had found the marker – the flat stone that Dick had unearthed yesterday.

The map showed where the marker was in the Treasure Room. By turning the map to match this bearing, we were able to see that each symbol on the map related to one wall within the Treasure Room. But we still had no idea what the symbols meant or where the Dragon was hidden.

"I've brought some chalk," suggested Dick. "Why don't we test the bricks in each wall and mark the ones we've searched?" Breaking his chalk into four pieces, Dick gave each of us a piece.

Painstakingly, we each took a wall, and, working from the bottom up, we tested each brick to see if one pulled out or pushed in to reveal a hiding place. With Dick's chalk, we kept track of all the bricks we had tested.

After several hours (with our chalk markings reaching about half way up each wall), Timmy's patience finally broke and he barked at us sharply, as if to say, 'Don't forget lunch again'!

We were so bitterly disappointed. We knew that this was our last chance to find the Dragon – this lost treasure that had captured our imagination and brought us to Riddle Island. But we daren't risk being late to meet Uncle Quentin. And we were ever so hungry (sometimes, a delicious picnic could be more appealing than even the most valuable treasure to the Five!). We looked at each other and seemed to come to an unspoken agreement. We made the difficult decision to abandon our search.

The walk back to camp was very quiet and solemn, even Timmy walked with his tail down and a sad expression on his face. We had searched and searched and found not a trace of the Royal Dragon. The mystery had come to a deflating end. Tomorrow we would return to Kirrin and prepare for the start of our school terms. All our efforts had come to nothing!

Without paying much attention to where we were walking we had arrived in the spot where our camp should be – but something was horribly wrong. Instead of our cosy tents and neat fire circle there was nothing but a bunch of scattered ashes and stones. Our camp looked like it had been ravaged! Our tarp was torn and flung out to sea (luckily, it had snagged on a rock and hadn't been washed away). Our large can of drinking water was overturned and empty. Our food store had been taken. Our tents (all except one which had been completely destroyed) and sleeping bags had disappeared. And apart from a single pan, all our gear was gone!

We stared at each other in a state of shock, Timmy growling deep in his throat. What had happened? A horrible realization hit us all at the same moment. We ran to the beach and made our second terrible discovery – our sailing boat was missing!

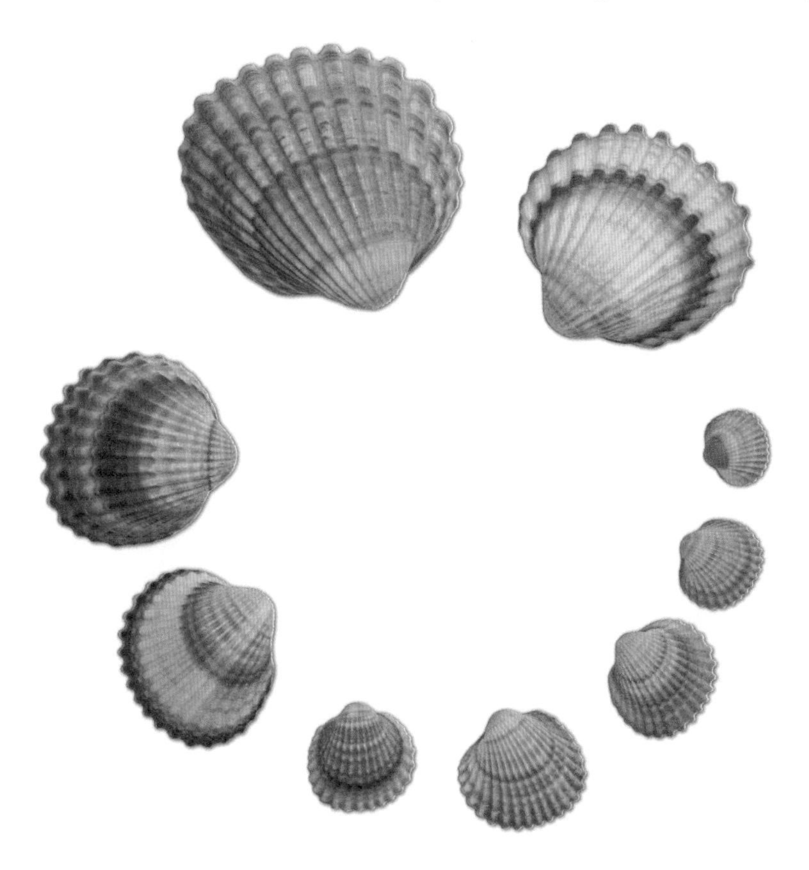

Chapter Eight

Stranded!

We were frightfully angry and confused. It was clear to us that someone had destroyed our camp – if one's tents, sleeping bags, food and gear have all vanished, the only possible culprit is a person, for no animal could be responsible for such a thing. What we couldn't understand was why anyone would deliberately steal our things and leave us stranded on Riddle Island?

None of us moved for several minutes, too shocked to know what to do. Finally, we all turned to look at Julian. He was (and is) a fine leader and just the type of person one wants to have around when adventures go wrong.

Julian was already planning what we were to do next.

"The first thing is to gather what's left of our scattered gear and review what's there. I'll do a circuit of the island to see if I can spot the sail boat. If I can't, then we'll have to figure out another way of getting back."

"Oh no," groaned George. "Father will be terribly cross if we don't meet him tonight."

Suddenly, Dick stopped short and called back to us. "Wait! Everyone stop! Don't move!"

We froze in our tracks. Dick had spotted a footprint near our campsite and it wasn't one of ours! It was a clue to who had stolen our boat. We got out of the way so Dick could examine the footprints. He pulled a notebook out of his pocket and briskly sketched the crime scene.

Do you know what to do when you run across a suspicious crime scene? If you want to be a proper sleuth, there are some important skills you'll need to learn …

BE YOUR OWN CSI

Investigate a crime scene like a pro

Even if your suspect has long gone from the scene of their misdeeds, you can still gain vital clues and information. Take our tips and your evidence will soon mount up.

CRIME SCENE

01. Choose a group leader to evaluate the clues and decide where next to search and what to look for.

02. Protect the scene and only allow one person to move around the area at a time. This will avoid the loss or disturbance of vital clues.

03. Divide the scene into a grid pattern so that your search will be systematic and organized. Assign an area to each member of your team.

04. Have different members of your team check the others' areas. A fresh pair of eyes can often turn up missed evidence.

05. Keep a record of the evidence as it is found.

EVIDENCE

WHAT TO LOOK FOR

- Strands of hair.
- Tiny pieces of string, fabric or fibres.
- Cigarette butts.
- Buttons.
- Gum wrappers.
- Train tickets.

HOW TO COLLECT EVIDENCE

01. Photograph or sketch the evidence you see and its location.

02. Pick the evidence up with plastic gloves or tweezers and put it into a small plastic bag.

03. Make sure you clearly label the bag with type, location and the name of the person who found it.

FOOTPRINTS

01. Enter the scene carefully, without stepping on any footprints or other evidence.

02. Look for footprints leading to and from the scene.

03. Photograph, sketch and make a cast of the prints.

04. Use the footprints to work out what happened at the crime scene from the tracks.

05. Exit the scene by stepping in your own footprints so that you don't disturb evidence.

TRACKING

- Measure the length and width of each footprint, so that you can tell different tracks apart.
- Measure each person's stride. The stride is the distance from the back heel of the left foot to the back heel of the right foot.
- Mark each set of tracks with tiny twigs. Now that you can tell the different prints apart, you can follow each person's trail.

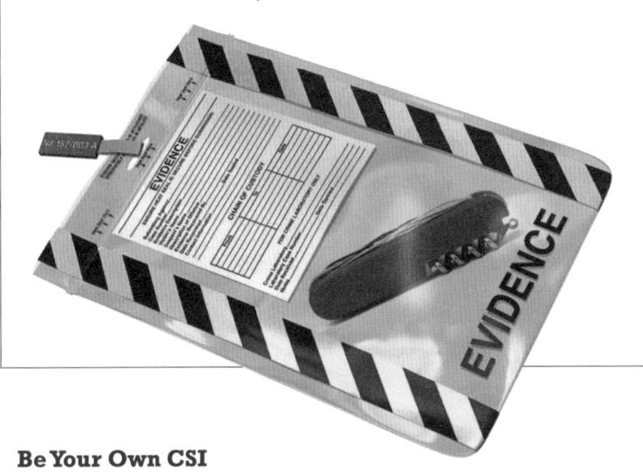

PRINT HINTS

The best piece of evidence you can gather as proof of a wrongdoer is a fingerprint. Never mind all the fancy stuff you've seen on screen. A few simple items will allow you to retrieve your own prints from anywhere.

You will need:

- **Pencil**
- **Coin**
- **Feather or small soft blusher brush**
- **Transparent tape**
- **Piece of white card**

01. When hunting for fingerprints, smooth surfaces will offer the best quality prints so look for glass, smooth metal, painted or varnished materials.

02. Break some of the lead from the pencil and use the coin to grind it into a fine graphite powder on a smooth flat surface.

03. Gently sprinkle the powder over the suspected fingerprint area.

04. Using the feather or brush, gently dust the powder away from the print. You must be extremely gentle doing this as dusting too hard will remove the print completely.

05. Once the print has been revealed, take a piece of tape and place the sticky side down squarely over your dusted print. Make sure you place it straight down and don't slip and smudge the print. Holding the tape at either end will ensure you can pick it back up again without it sticking to the surface too much.

06. Lift the tape and stick it to your piece of card to reveal your print. Keep it for examination.

D.K. 28th August, 1959

Calamity has struck!

Some vicious fiend has robbed us of our gear and our sailing boat! Fortunately they left their prints in the soft sand. I immediately had the rest of the Five stay still as I examined the beach for clues. I must say, I rather enjoyed playing the detective. Certainly, all those Secret Seven novels I've read have taught me a lot! Perhaps I shall be a real private investigator when I am grown? This is how I went about my investigation.

At once I noticed that there was a deep dragline where the Island Drifter had been pushed into the sea. The footprints that led to the sea were distinctly those of a woman's high-heeled shoes.

As Julian pointed out it would have been perfect if we had our things. We could have made a plaster cast of her prints.

I continued to follow the different sets of tracks on the beach. I found ours and Timmy's. Then I made an exciting discovery, prints that didn't match ours, nor those of the woman's high-heeled shoes.

That's how she (whoever she was) got the Island Drifter into the sea. She had help! And she left a very important clue behind! Snagged in the rocky surf at the beach's edge, I found a heel that had clearly broken off one of her shoes! It matches the prints exactly! What a piece of evidence that is. I have wrapped it in my handkerchief and will hand it over to the police as soon as we get back to civilisation.

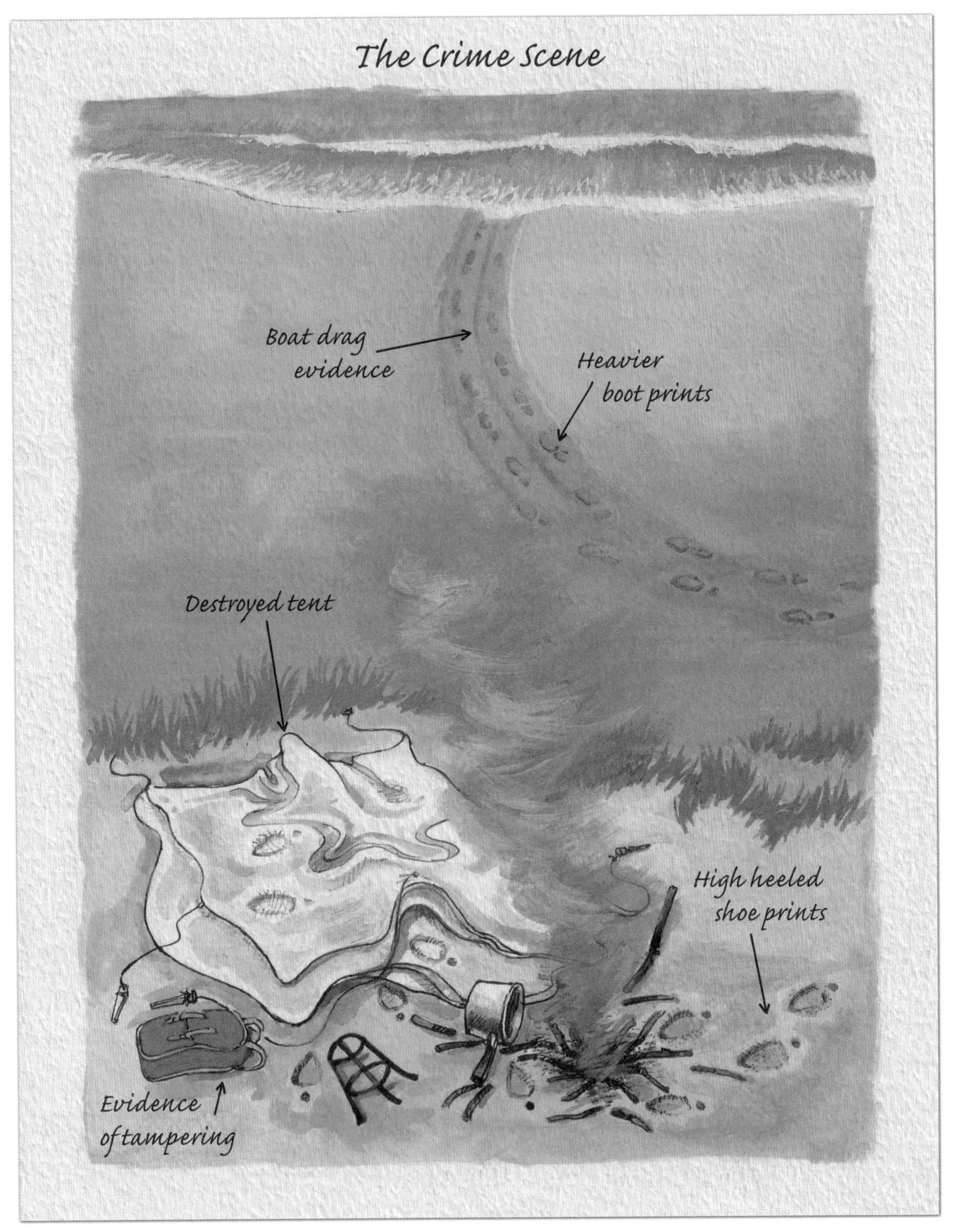
The Crime Scene
Boat drag evidence
Heavier boot prints
Destroyed tent
High heeled shoe prints
Evidence of tampering

Dick compiled his evidence, and proudly presented it to us. When he showed us the red heel he had uncovered, Anne gasped and then went very pale.

"Oh, dear me!" declared Anne, visibly upset. "It's her, isn't it? Miss Butlerton, the reporter. And it's all my fault!"

Dick and George looked at Anne in astonishment. But Julian looked resigned.

"It's not your fault, Anne," he said. " Look everyone, I am terribly sorry, this whole thing is my fault. I knew when George was kidnapped that Butlerton was behind it. I should have been more careful."

"How did you know?" asked Dick.

"Anne told me," replied Julian. "She had let it slip out to Butlerton where we were going. That's how the reporter knew to follow us."

"I knew she was a bad sort," spat George. "And she always wears those stupid shoes!"

"But ... I mean to say ... WHY?" stuttered Dick.

"I believe that she is after the Royal Dragon of Siam for herself," Julian explained. "She just made up that she's writing a story about our great-great-great-grandfather so she could snoop on us and try to get those papers out of Uncle," he concluded.

"And she was talking about half a treasure map! Perhaps she has the other half of the map!" shouted Dick.

"We can't worry about that now," sighed Julian. "We need to salvage what we can here and work out what we're going to do. Come on."

We saved everything we could from the campsite. All that was left of our well-ordered camp and stores was the large tarpaulin we had used as a ground sheet, one pan, a little cocoa, and the gear we had taken to the tower with us. We had very little water and no food. We didn't even have a compass between us!

There was no way to get back to St Agnes and no way to inform Uncle Quentin of our delay – or even of our location! In fact, the only people who knew we were on Riddle Island were the dastardly Butlerton and Harbourmaster Rivers. He didn't know we planned to return that day, so he wouldn't be looking for us. What a predicament!

Julian told us that the most important thing was to stay calm. He got Anne busy heating up the cocoa for us. He asked George to gather fresh firewood and Dick to fill our empty water can at the cistern in the Martello tower. At least we knew it was drinking water and we'd boil it before drinking to make sure it was safe.

"I'm going off to catch us some fish for dinner," said Julian.

"But you haven't a rod!" cried Dick.

"I shall improvize, little brother," chuckled Julian. "After all, we are adventurers *par excellence* and we've made it out of much worse scrapes."

The Diary of Julian Kirrin - *Kirrin Cottage*

28th August, morning

That dreadful Butlerton woman has stolen our food and gear! I haven't let on to the others how dire our situation is, it would only make things worse, but this is one of those rare times when I am feeling more than a bit pessimistic.

Above all else I have to remain calm. We have no supplies, and we'll need to build a shelter for the night with that bit of tarp and our ropes.

"What will we do about the treasure?" asked George.

But we can't think about that now. Besides, we hunted that room very thoroughly. I have a feeling we're missing an important clue. A clue that fiendish reporter must have!

Anyway, I must find us some dinner. Anne was shocked to hear that dinner might involve a rabbit or two, but I won't have us go hungry.

"I don't care if I am starving. I still won't eat a poor defenceless bunny!" answered Anne, stubbornly.

Dick reminded her that I always came back with a fine catch of fish. Anne took a bit of comfort from his words.

I much prefer fishing to hunting rabbits so I walked along the shore to a calm deep inlet that would likely hold our dinner. I noticed that the tide was out, creating some tidal pools along the shore that should contain some mussels and clams, too.

Some time ago, I found an article about fishing without the proper equipment – I'm terribly glad that I cut it out and kept it in my journal. It will be invaluable to us today!

HOW TO CATCH FISH IN THE WILD

Trapped near water? Worried about what you are going to do for food? Some simple skills will not only keep you alive but also see you sampling a seafood supper before you know it. Of course, carrying an emergency fishing kit with line, hook and float is always a sensible idea on any trip.

HOOKED

Hooks can be made from almost anything, with bent nails and pins being the easiest. But even the novice can make themselves a couple of different hooks from a small piece of wood and a bit of simple knife work.

GORGE

01. Take a piece of hardwood around 2.5 – 3cm long and sharpen each end into a point. Any material can be used as long as you can shape it into a point at the end.

02. Cut a small notch in one side and secure your line around the centre of the gorge using the notch to stop it slipping.

03. Attach your bait by sliding the gorge lengthways into it. When the bait is taken the gorge will flip horizontally and hook your fish.

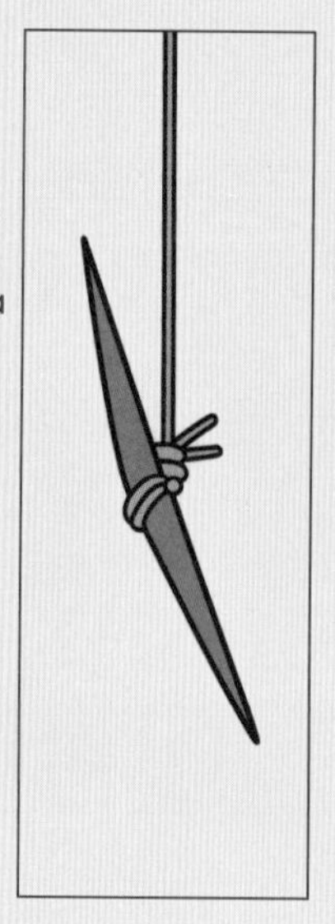

WOODEN HOOK

01. Find a sharp piece of metal, wire, bone or even a nail. This will be your point.

02. Take a small piece of hardwood 2.5cm long and around 6mm in diameter. This will be your shank.

03. Cut a notch in the end and secure the piece of metal or whatever you are going to use as the point.

04. Push the point into the notch so that it sticks out at around a 30-degree angle from the shank.

05. Tie a piece of string or twine tightly around the bottom of the notch to tighten the shank and prevent the point falling out.

06. Attach a line, add bait, and fish away.

STAKEOUT

Now you have your hooks it doesn't mean you are forced to stay in one place with a line in your hand in order to catch some food. A simple hands-free way to fill your survival larder is to make a stakeout trap.

01. Find a place where you know fish will pass through regularly. This can be an inlet, stream, river or tidal area.

02. Take two flexible saplings and drive them into the riverbed a suitable width apart, this will depend on the width of the river where you are catching your fish.

03. Tie a line between the saplings under the water so it lies a few centimetres above the bed of the river.

04. Attach two vertical lines onto the main line ensuring they aren't long enough to tangle around the support poles or each other.

05. Attach a hook to the end of each line. These can be ready-made hooks or ones you have made yourself.

06. Add the bait then leave the trap and return regularly to check.

SPEAR FISHING

01. Take a length of hardwood around 90cm in length.

02. Using your knife, sharpen one end into a point. If you can split the end into a two-pronged tip this will work even better.

03. Find your fish by watching shallow water, remember not to let your shadow fall across the water as this will scare the fish away.

04. Position your spear tip just above the water and wait.

05. When a fish is in position below your spear, drive the spear down with a hard, thrusting, movement.

06. Don't be surprised if it takes a while to catch anything as spear fishing takes the most patience, reaction speed and skill of any type of fishing.

TRAPS

There are many ways to make fish traps, from making your own net from twine, to shaping intricate traps from chicken wire. The simplest trap of all, and extremely effective when near the sea, is the pool trap.

01. Wait until low tide and find a large exposed rock pool.

02. Using stones build a wall around the rock pool. Ensure the height of your wall is sufficient to allow the water in at high tide.

03. Wait for the higher tide to pass and the water to retreat and then check your pool. By increasing the height of the edges of the pool, the outgoing tide will have left you with an array of fish and seafood to feast upon.

Julian arrived back at camp and produced two fine plaice and a handful of clams for our dinner – all caught with his homemade fishing equipment! He was surprised to find not only a blazing fire with water boiling in the pan, but also an emergency shelter that we had set up with the tarpaulin and our ropes around two stout trees on the beach.

"Go on, Anne," coaxed George. "Tell Julian your discovery."

"What's this?" asked Julian. "Nothing else has gone wrong for us I hope!"

"No, Julian. It's just that I've figured out something about Butlerton. It confirms our suspicions that she's behind all the nastiness that has befallen us since we set ourselves to solving the mystery of the Royal Dragon."

"Well? Come on, Anne, do tell me," said Julian impatiently. "What have you learned?"

"It's actually something you learned, Julian – when you discovered that Turnbolte and Lunbertot were anagrams. Well, Butlerton is an anagram, too. It has the exact same letters in it as the jewel thief's name," explained Anne.

Julian thought for a moment and then realized that Anne was right.

"We think that Lunbertot, or Turnbolte, or whatever his real name was, is an ancestor of the reporter's," continued Dick. "Just as the Captain is an ancestor of ours."

"I think you're absolutely right, old chap," responded Julian. "And Butlerton's turned out to be just as crooked as her ancestor was ..."

George interrupted us to say that we had to get a move on – she predicted a violent thunderstorm heading our way. She said we'd have lightning later and that we should eat and get under our shelter as quickly as possible.

We others just saw a clear sky above, slowly darkening to dusk. But we knew that George, who had grown up in the outdoors and understood nature's ways much better than we did, had an uncanny ability to read the weather. You'll find George's weather wisdom on the next few pages. If you want to get right back to the hunt for the Royal Dragon of Siam turn to page 215.

OLD WIVES TALES THAT ARE TRUE

RED SKY AT NIGHT, SHEPHERD'S DELIGHT; PINK SKY IN THE MORNING, SAILOR'S WARNING

This old saying does have some meteorological foundation, at least in the Northern Hemisphere, where storms tend to follow jet streams. Jet streams are westerly winds, which flow from the west towards the east.

At dawn and dusk, when the sun is low in the sky, sunlight travels through the atmosphere more than at any other time of day. The red end of the spectrum of light is reflected back off clouds.

The sun rises in the east and sets in the west. If, at sunrise, there are a lot of broken clouds in the west, the sky will appear pink. As this cloud is in the west it will be heading towards us, carried by the gulf stream. Approaching clouds bring with them a chance of rain and storms, so sailors should be warned of rough weather ahead.

Similarly, if there are a lot of red clouds in the evening they will be in the east and will have already passed over us, leaving clear skies behind them and signalling to shepherds that a clear night for their flock is ahead.

MACKEREL SKY, NEVER LONG WET, NEVER LONG DRY

This proverb has nothing to do with the colour of the sky, but with the formation of the clouds (see pages 210 and 211). A mackerel sky is a sky where the cloud is broken up, resembling the scales of a mackerel.

The saying does have some truth to it though. When the clouds are spread out in mackerel scales it is usually an indicator of moisture at lower levels and of surface temperature instability. This can lead to scattered showers never lasting long, but never far away.

RAIN BEFORE SEVEN, FINE BY ELEVEN

This proverb comes from the fact that constant rain never usually lasts more than four hours. In some temperate latitudes, where weather fronts become slow moving, rain can last more than four hours, and sometimes does. However, in most Northern Hemisphere locations, if it is raining at seven it is unlikely that the rain will continue for long, leaving the skies clear by eleven.

CLEAR MOON; FROST SOON

If the moon is clear, it means that the atmosphere is clear and free of clouds. As a result of there being no cloud cover, the surface of the Earth cools much faster than on a night when there are clouds. If the temperature is low, and there is no wind, frost is likely to form.

MOSS DRY, SUNNY SKY; MOSS WET, RAIN WE'LL GET

This isn't simply stating the obvious (that if it rains, moss will get wet); this proverb recommends using moss as a way to predict approaching storms. When a storm is near, the air is often full of moisture. Moss acts like a sponge absorbing that moisture and becoming wet itself. If the moss is dry, it means there is no moisture in the air, and less chance of rain.

HALO ROUND THE MOON, RAIN OR SNOW SOON

A halo around the moon is caused by a layer of cirrus clouds (see page 210) made of ice crystals. These cirrus clouds are often an indication of a warm front and low pressure. Rain or snow often follow this low pressure. It is not a definite test, but the brighter the halo, the more likely the proverb is to be true.

HOW TO READ THE CLOUDS

Clues to what the weather is doing, and what it is going to do, are all around us. All it takes to predict most types of weather is simply look at the clouds. Knowing the basic cloud types and what they foretell will see you much more prepared for the weather and any problems it may bring.

CIRRUS

Cirrus clouds have a thin and wispy appearance and are found very high in the sky, above 18,000 feet. Cirrus clouds predict neutral to fair weather, although they can warn of the approach of a storm front if the weather has been cooler before their appearance.

CIRROCUMULUS

Appearing as ripples, Cirrocumulus are also referred to as mackerel sky due to their appearance being similar to fish scales. They can be found at around the 18,000 feet mark. These clouds can predict a local rainstorm but usually precede a much larger weather front approaching.

ALTOCUMULUS

Between 6,000 and 20,000 feet is the place to find these 'string of pearls' looking clouds. A large coverage means that a significant amount of moisture is on the move over a large distance. This denotes a cold front moving in that during warm weather could precede a thunderstorm.

STRATUS

The lowest lying of the cloud formations, stratus are found at the 6,000 feet mark. They appear so large due to their proximity to the ground. Stratus clouds are uniform in their appearance and most common along coasts and valleys where they are created by a high moisture content. Stratus clouds can deliver small amounts of drizzle or snow but never a massive downpour.

NIMBOSTRATUS

Found at a similar height to Stratus clouds, Nimbostratus are the dark foreboding clouds that everyone will recognize as rain clouds. These heavy, low lying clouds are often the precursor to a heavy thunderstorm.

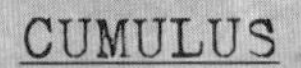

CUMULUS

The typical summer clouds, Cumulus are the cotton-wool looking clouds with clear sky between them. Fair weather is ahead when you see these clouds. They shouldn't be confused with Cumulonimbus which have a very different meaning.

CUMULONIMBUS

Similar in appearance to the Cumulus, the Cumulonimbus denotes an approaching thunderstorm with large downpours expected as well as thunder and lightning. If Cumulonimbus are seen then rain will soon follow.

HOW TO SURVIVE LIGHTNING

The sky has turned dark and the ominous rumble of thunder can be heard approaching. Before long the darkened clouds start flashing with the oncoming lightning storm. What can you do to keep from being struck?

BEFORE LIGHTNING STRIKES

01. You can tell roughly how far a lightning storm is from you by counting the seconds between hearing a thunderclap and seeing a lightning bolt.

02. Divide the number of seconds between thunder and lightning by 5, and you will arrive at the storm's approximate distance in miles. For instance, if the time between lightning and thunder is 5 seconds then the storm is around 1 mile away.

03. You need to get to safety when a storm is about 6 miles away, or 30 seconds between the crash of the thunder and the flash of the lightning.

REDUCE YOUR RISK

01. Lightning is attracted to water. If you're in the water, get out and move a good distance away from the water.

02. Lightning is also attracted to metal. Take off your backpack if it contains metal in the zippers and the support poles. Put the backpack a safe distance of at least 15 metres from yourself. Also remove any clothing with large zips and move these away from you.

03. If you are in a group, spread out at least 30 metres apart. If lightning strikes one person, it can pass through the ground and hit any others close by.

04. Avoid small sheds and temporary shelters as the lightning may well be attracted to these, especially if they contain metal.

05. Keep away from overhead power and telephone lines and stay away from any metal pipe work that may be around.

SURVIVE THE STORM

01. Lightning will strike the tallest thing in the area. Don't stand under tall or single trees, communication towers, flag poles, street lights or metal fences.

02. Keep your head low. You don't want to be the tallest thing in the area.

03. Lightning will travel along the ground electrocuting anything in its path.

04. Make sure the part of your body touching the ground is as small as possible. Crouch down and keep your feet close together, staying on the balls of your feet. Don't touch the ground with your hands. Don't lie down.

AFTER THE STORM

Lightning can still strike up to a half-hour after you hear the last crash of thunder. Don't come out of your safe place until the danger is well past.

Don't believe the myth that rubber-soled shoes will protect you, as this has been proven wrong by more than one victim.

Anne's Diary - 29th August, 1959

Makeshift camp on Riddle Island beach, dawn

Dear Diary,

The lightning was fierce last night but fortunately was far off to sea. The distance of the thunder was a blessing. Tim does love to howl along with big booming claps of thunder. Thankfully, his canine chorus was kept to a minimum!

Diary, I am ever so grateful for my dear big brother's ability to stay calm and take care of the Five! Julian caught us some lovely fish and Dick was a sport and cleaned and cooked them. Delicious! Even Timmy had his share. (What would I have done if Julian had come back with a rabbit! I just couldn't eat it. I couldn't . . .)

I am so terribly frightened, but I won't let on to the others. No one comes to these tiny islands. What if we're stuck here for a long time? And what of Uncle Quentin and Aunt Fanny? They will be beside themselves with worry by now. At least, I'm sure Aunt Fanny will. If Uncle has actually told her that we missed our rendezvous, of course. He is so awfully forgetful that perhaps he hasn't . . .

How will we ever get back to St Agnes? It's much too far to swim, and I'm not a strong swimmer anyway. Dick and George almost seem to be enjoying themselves. Julian says we must send rescue signals today. I'm waiting for the others to wake up. We are to build three large fires on the top of the hill so that any passing boats will see them and rescue us. I shan't let those signal fires go out for even a second!

I'm determined to be brave, Diary. I feel so terribly responsible for our misfortune. I was flattered by Miss Butlerton and told her things I shouldn't have. I trusted a liar and a thief! I only hope I get the chance to make it up to the others . . .

HOW TO SEND RESCUE SIGNALS

You are stranded miles from anywhere and your only hope of rescue is to signal for help. Here's how.

THE RULE OF THREE

Three is the universal signal of danger or distress, so remember that however you signal you are more likely to get a response if you do it in groups of three.

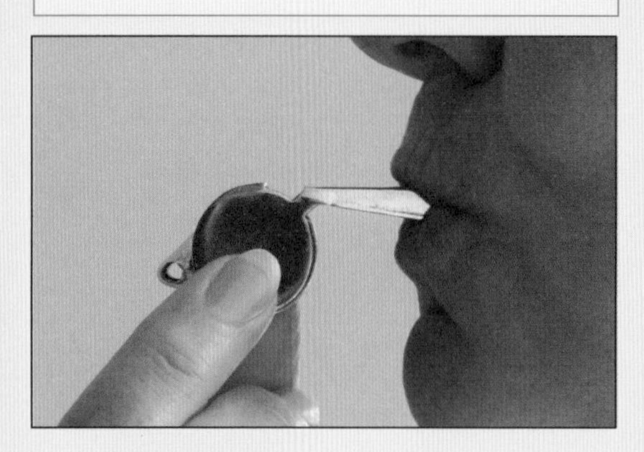

WHISTLE AWAY

01. Whistles are excellent for signalling over short distances and will carry much further than your voice.

02. Whistles are also ideal for signalling in the dark, fog or heavily wooded areas.

03. Remember that three sharp blasts will draw more attention than one long one.

MIRROR, MIRROR

01. A mirror or shiny, reflective object is a useful tool whose signal can be seen for miles. Of course, mirror signalling will only work if you have sunlight.

02. Hold the mirror in one hand and adjust it until you catch the sun's reflection.

03. Hold your hand a small distance apart and make a 'V' with your fingers.

04. Adjust the mirror so the light from the sun reflects between the 'V' of your fingers.

05. Point the signal towards the horizon and wobble the mirror to send the signal, remember three flashes at a time.

FIRE IT UP

01. Build three large pyramid shaped fires and space them around 15 metres apart in a triangular shape, this makes it easier for aircraft to spot.

02. If near the sea, pick the highest point you can find that is visible from the water to build your fire. Build three large fires in a line. This lets passing ships know you are in distress.

03. If possible use evergreen branches for your fire as this will cause your fire to burn fast and bright.

04. Keep plenty of firewood on hand to keep your fire going.

USE WHAT YOU'VE GOT

01. Use the items you have around you, and if you can find a clearing spread out three piles that can be seen from the air, e.g. tents, jackets or rucksacks.

02. If trapped near a beach use nearby vegetation to make three piles in a triangular shape, remembering to space them out so they can be seen from the air.

03. Carve out the letters SOS as large as possible in the sand, although this will only attract aircraft during daylight.

From the desk of Georg~~ina~~e Kirrin

August 29th, 1959

This is no good at all! We can't count on a ship passing by to rescue us. Mr Rivers told me that the ocean currents between here and St Agnes are highly irregular. Most boats avoid this island.

We cannot wait. We must make our own way off Riddle Island.

I've got a plan. We will build a raft and sail it back to St Agnes! It's the only option we have. We must get back or Father will be crosser than I am sure I have ever seen him. If we are late for school term I am certain I will be held back a year!

A raft to carry all of the Five would have to be enormous. We don't have the time to build something that large, and it would be much harder to navigate anyway. I've got it worked out, though. Julian and I will take the raft across and Dick and Anne will stay on Riddle Island with Timmy to guard them.

I hate to leave my Timothy behind but it's just too risky to have him on the raft with us. I'll let on to Anne that Timmy will stay to protect her and Dick. Otherwise, the reality of what we're up against might scare her. The raft crossing is going to be terribly dangerous.

I shall tell Julian what I'm planning. First, though, I want to get down my plan for building our raft.

Later that day, we let Anne in on our raft-making plans. She was immediately worried and Julian quickly assured her that he and George would be perfectly safe. In fact, George would need Anne's help to make life jackets, while the boys constructed the raft.

Julian and Dick collected logs, vines and our ropes. When everything was gathered in one place, they constructed the raft according to George's plan. After a few hours of hard work, the raft was seaworthy. The girls had prepared the life vests and filled two canteens with water, one each for George and Julian. They would set off at first light the next morning.

We didn't talk about the journey ahead of them. Instead, we discussed when we might have time to come back to Riddle Island for the Royal Dragon. It would be too cold during our next holiday break. We wouldn't be able to return until next spring. We wondered whether Butlerton would simply wait for us to be out of the way before coming to claim the treasure for herself?

"I don't think she can," said Anne quietly. "She doesn't have all the clues we have. If she knew that the Dragon was on Riddle Island, she wouldn't have stranded us here."

"I do believe you're right, Anne," mused Julian. "I think she was trying to get hold of our papers and thought we'd be silly enough to leave them in our camp."

"Grown ups are always underestimating us kids," grumbled Dick.

"We'll show her," said George. "We'll get back to St Agnes and send someone back for you three. And then, I suppose, I'll have to call Father and face his wrath. He will be cross, won't he?" she asked.

"He'll be steaming!" chuckled Dick. "I almost wish I could be there to see him explode."

This made all of us laugh, despite our sorry situation, until Julian declared that everything was prepared for tomorrow's journey.

"Hang on," cried George. "We don't have a compass! How'll we find our way back to St Agnes?"

"I've got it worked out, George," said Julian. "You don't need a compass to find your way ... "

HOW TO BUILD AN ESCAPE RAFT

If you are stuck on an island with the mainland too far away to even consider swimming to safety, it's up to you to find a safe and secure way to get not only yourself, but also anyone else who may be with you, to safety.

PICK YOUR POSITION

Building a sturdy log raft will take strength and determination. There will be lots of heavy lifting involved, and also the use of an axe or chopping implement.

To make a successful raft you will need plenty of buoyancy, but the raft also needs to be light enough to actually move into the water from your construction area.

Pick a work area in which to build your raft that is near your launch position. If the water is shallow enough, and you feel confident, you could even build your raft in the water to reduce the amount you will have to move it in order to set sail.

SELECT AND COLLECT

You will need to plan the size of your raft to accommodate the number of people that need transporting. As a guide, a three-and-a-half metre by two-and-a-half metre raft will comfortably carry two people.

Take a dozen three-and-a-half-metre long by around 10–15cm in diameter logs. These will form your main deck.

Collect two, slightly smaller in diameter, logs that are just over two metres in length. These will become your cross supports.

Find yourself plenty of lengths of something to bind the logs with. This can be fibrous bark or even strong seaweed strands.

BUILD YOUR RAFT

Take your longer deck logs and place them side by side so the ends line up and they form the basic shape of your raft.

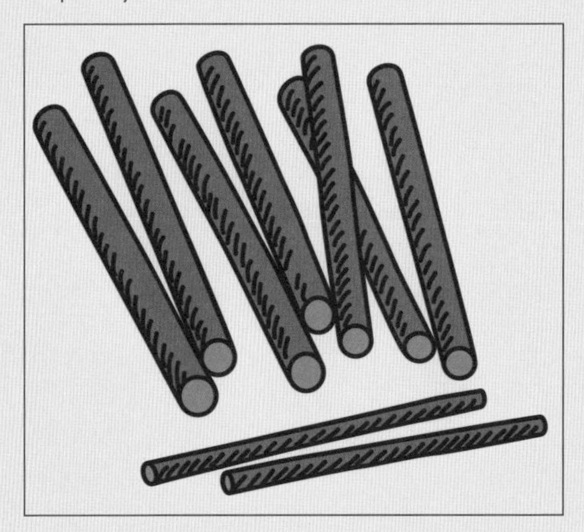

Half a metre from one end of each log, use an axe or saw to cut a four-centimetre-deep dovetail. Repeat this at the other end of the logs.

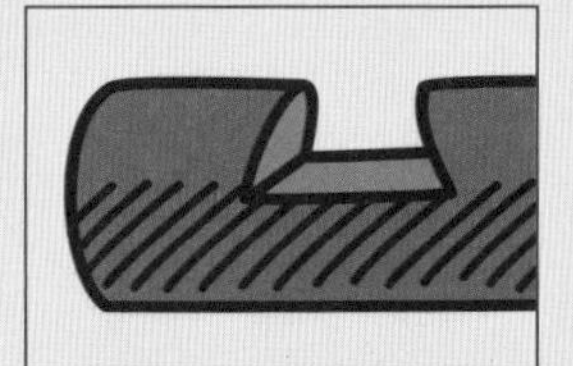

Line up the logs so that the dovetails are all in line. Take one of the two-metre logs and slide this through the dovetails. Bind the logs together using

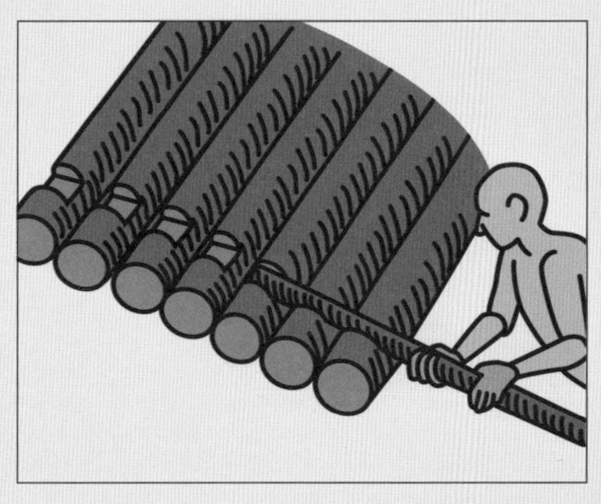

whatever binding material you have found. Repeat the process on the other end of the raft.

Turn the raft over and collect some dry ferns, brush or whatever you can find to cover the deck and provide a dry footing on your raft.

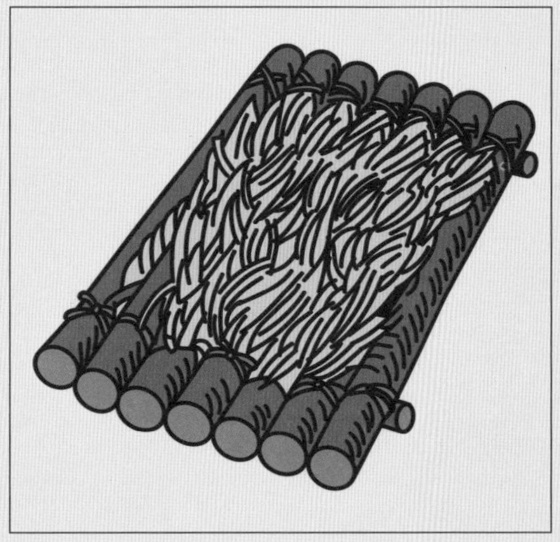

SAILS AND STUFF

Of course a basic log raft has no real steering abilities so navigation can be a bit hit and miss. To rectify this, a simple sail can be made using branches and tarpaulin, while using oars can not only provide a means of navigation, but also power for those times when there isn't enough wind to sail alone.

HOW TO MAKE AN EMERGENCY FLOTATION DEVICE

You are almost home but it involves crossing a large expanse of water. No matter how safe your vessel, it is only sensible to give yourself an extra line of defence with a personal flotation device. Time is short and you only have what is to hand, so it's time to get creative.

PLASTIC BAGS

01. Take two plastic bags and open the necks wide before filling them with air.

02. Using twine, string or whatever you can find, tie up the ends to seal the air inside.

03. Tie the two bags together with string. Place a bag under each arm so they are behind your back and the string joining them is across your chest.

04. Ensure that you have large enough bags and enough of them to support your weight before using them in an emergency situation.

TROUSERS

01. Knot the bottom of each trouser leg and close the fly and buttons.

02. Wet the trousers as this will help trap air in the legs.

03. Swing the trousers around to trap air and quickly submerge them under the water to trap the air in the legs. If you are already in the water this can be done by flipping the trousers over your head.

04. You may have to re-inflate the trousers a number of times if crossing a large area of water.

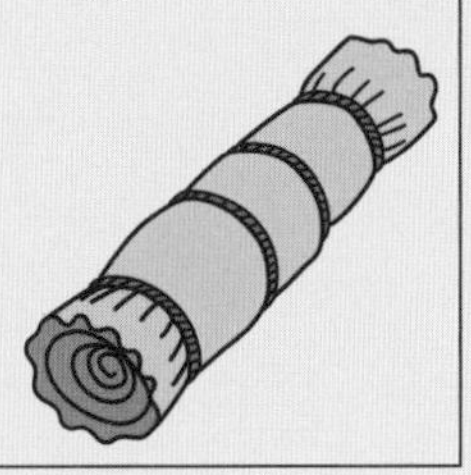

TARPS AND PONCHOS

01. Take a tarp or waterproof poncho and lay flat on the ground.

02. Collect as much green vegetation as you can find and lay it across the longest side of your tarp in a thick line.

03. Roll the tarp or poncho up like a long sausage so that the roll is at least 20 centimetres in diameter.

04. Tie the ends of the tarp securely with at least two ties along the roll as well, to keep it closed.

05. The roll can be worn either around the waist, across the chest or over one shoulder and under the other arm.

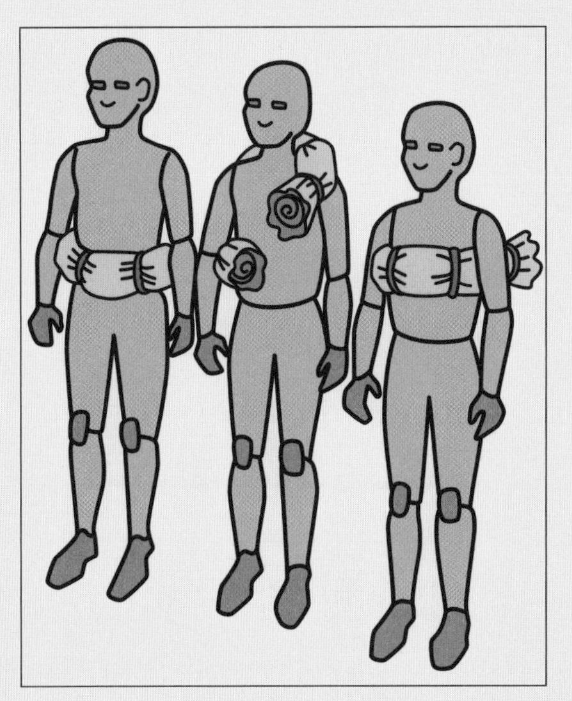

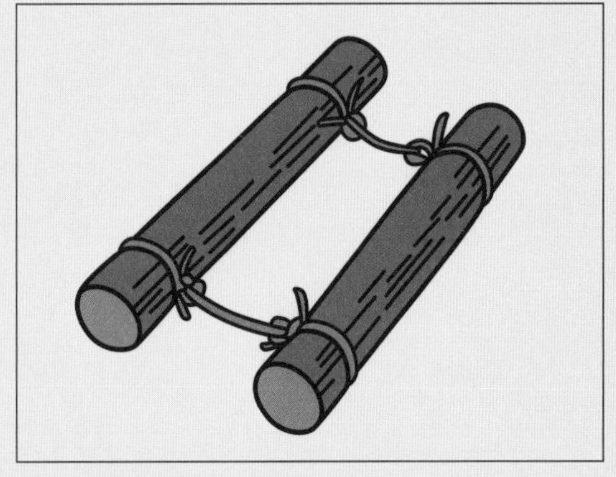

SIMPLE LOG FLOTATION

01. Find two small logs that will float.

02. Using two pieces of string, seaweed or whatever you can find, tie the ends of each log together so they are parallel to each other and around 60 centimetres apart.

03. Sit between the two logs with your back against one and your legs over the other.

FIND DIRECTION WITHOUT A COMPASS

You know that safety lies only a few miles away to the northeast of your position. Having lost all your equipment, including your all-important compass, how are you going to avoid ending your days lost and lonely in the wilderness?

WATCH METHOD

Using a standard analogue watch it is possible to determine the compass points. Make sure your watch isn't set to daylight saving time (see later for what to do if it is).

NORTHERN HEMISPHERE

Hold your watch horizontally and point the hour hand towards the sun.

Halve the angle between the hour hand and the 12 o'clock mark on the dial. This will give you the north-south line.

SOUTHERN HEMISPHERE

Hold your watch horizontally and point the 12 o'clock mark on the dial towards the sun.

Halve the angle between the 12 o'clock mark and the hour hand. This will give you the north-south line.

DAYLIGHT SAVING HELP

If your watch is set to daylight saving time simply use the 1 o'clock marker instead of the 12.

WATCHLESS! WHAT NOW?

Don't worry if you have a digital watch, it is still possible to find direction. Quickly draw a watch face on a piece of paper with the current time, indicated by the hands on your drawing, and continue as if you had a normal watch.

TIPS

If you are not sure which end of the line you have come up with is north and which is south simply remember that the sun rises in the east and sets in the west. Before midday the sun will be in the east and in the west after midday.

STAR GAZING

For many years mariners have used the stars for navigation and with some simple practice so can you; of course these tips will only apply if you are in the Northern Hemisphere.

CONSTELLATION CONSTERNATION

There are two main constellations to learn to aid you in night navigation. These are Cassiopeia and Ursa Major (also known as the Big Dipper or the Plough). Using these two constellations it is possible to find the North Star. The Big Dipper and Cassiopeia are always opposite each other and orbit around the North Star counter-clockwise. Once you have found the North Star it's a simple matter of drawing an imaginary line directly from it to the Earth below to find north on land

CASSIOPEIA
A five star constellation that looks similar to a 'W' on its side. Much like Ursa Major there is also a star that shows a direct line to the North Star. Note the centre star of the constellation and look directly left to find the North Star.

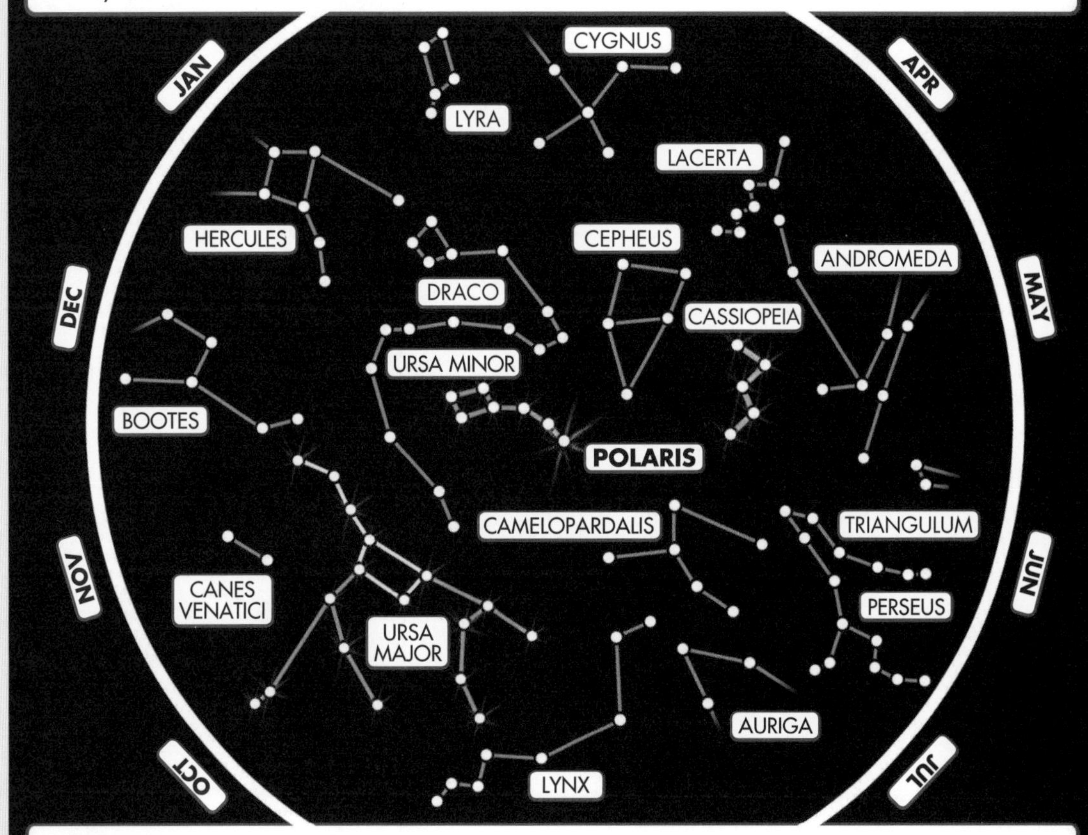

URSA MAJOR
Ursa Major, also known as the Great Bear, contains the group of stars known as the Big Dipper or Plough. This group of stars, professionally referred to as an asterism, contain two stars that point directly to the North Star. The two stars that make up the lowest point of the asterism form a straight line towards the all-important North Star.

HOW TO MAKE A COMPASS

Finding yourself lost without any idea of your bearings is bad enough. Being lost without your bearings or a compass is even worse. How do you find your way back to safety? Time is running out and only some quick thinking will save you.

FLOATING COMPASS

YOU WILL NEED

- Sewing needle/nail/straightened paper clip
- Bowl/cup
- Magnet
- Water
- Leaf or cork

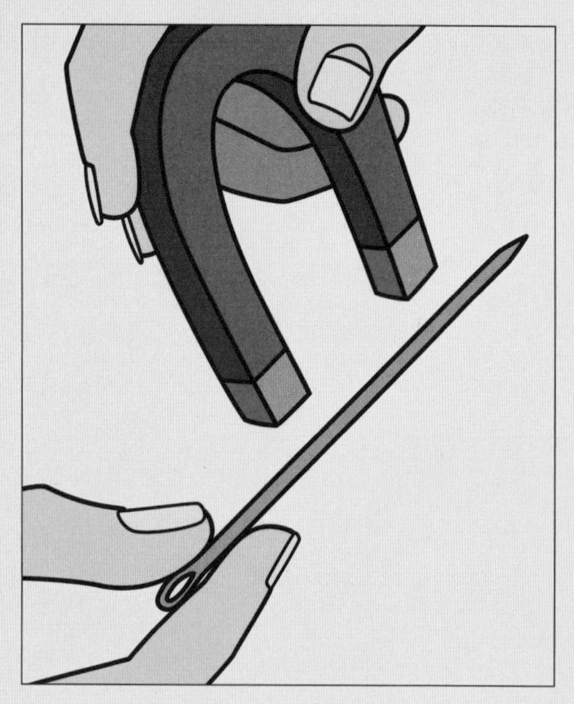

01. Stroke the needle (or whatever you are using) from the blunt end towards the pointed end, across the magnet 60 times (more is better). Remember to keep stroking in the same direction each time.

02. Check the needle is magnetized by touching it to a pin or small metallic item.

03. Gently bend the leaf and thread the needle through it. Allow the leaf to lie flat. If using a cork push the needle through the side of it.

04. Fill the bowl, cup or any non-metallic item with water and float your leaf on top of the water.

05. Make sure you move the magnet you used at least 60cm away from the container, also make sure there are no metal items nearby.

06. Move the needle so that it gently spins on top of the water.

07. Wait a short while and the needle will stop spinning with the pointed end showing the direction of North.

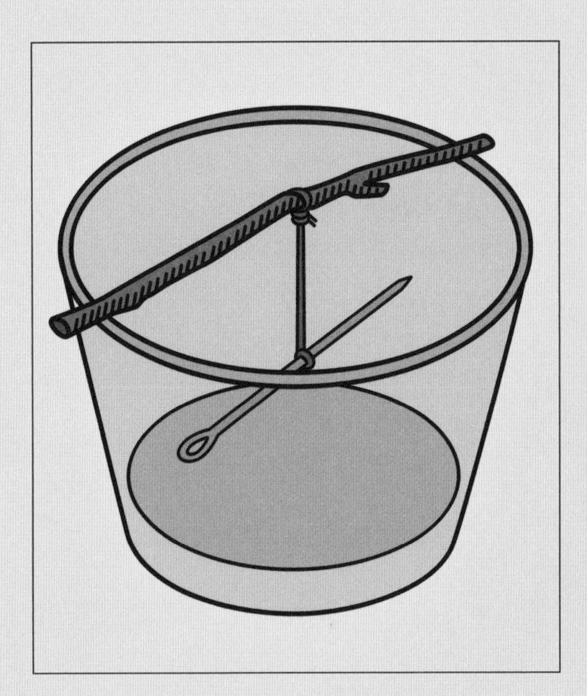

HANGING COMPASS

YOU WILL NEED

- Plastic cup or beaker
- Magnet
- Piece of thread
- Needle or small nail
- Pencil or short stick

01. Rub the magnet, from the blunt end of the needle towards the pointed end, remembering to continue stroking in the same direction. Do this around 60 times.

02. Tie one end of the thread around the middle of the needle and the other end around the centre of the pencil or stick.

03. Place the pencil across the rim of the cup so the needle hangs into the cup. Make sure the needle is not touching the cup; wrap the thread around the pencil if you need to raise the needle higher in the cup.

04. Wait for the needle to settle and the pointed end will point towards north.

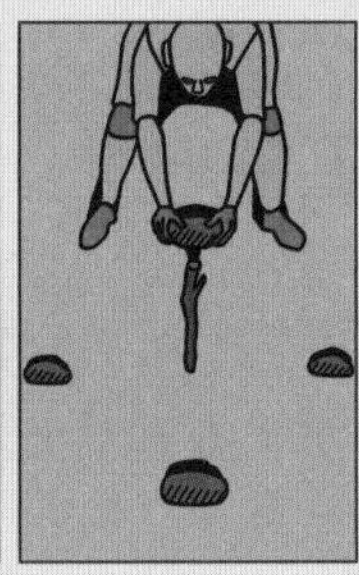

ROCK COMPASS

YOU WILL NEED

- 50cm stick
- Two large rocks
- Two small rocks

01. Find a sunny clearing or slope.

02. Dig a hole and bury the bottom 15cm of the stick in the ground.

03. Early in the morning place a small rock at the tip of the shadow made by the stick. This marks west.

04. Wait until the afternoon.

05. When the shadow has moved and is the same length as it was in the morning, put another small rock at the tip of the stick shadow once again, to mark east.

06. Stand between the two rocks so the first rock is by your left foot and the second is by your right. Place one of the large rocks directly in front of you about 30cm away from the stick. This is north.

07. Turn around and repeat step six again placing a large rock the same distance from the stick on the opposite side. This will be south. Mark this rock to make it look different from the rest.

08. You should now be left with a stick surrounded by four rocks at equal distances from it, with the four main points of the compass clearly defined by the rocks.

From the desk of Georg~~ina~~e Kirrin

August 30th, 1959

We ate a light breakfast of freshly caught fish cooked over our campfire. Anne packed up the canteens of water that we would take on our journey. We loaded the raft with a few supplies and secured them with ropes so they wouldn't fall overboard. Then Julian and I tied on the life jackets (of sorts) that Anne and I made yesterday.

We gave Dick and Anne big hugs and promised we'd send a boat for them as quickly as we could. I squeezed Tim goodbye so hard he yelped. He made to come with me as Julian and I dragged the raft to the surf. I had to be quite stern with him to get him to stay.

We paddled the raft through the surf and out into the open sea, moving about gingerly on the raft. We hit a bit of a calm spot and took the time to fill the leaks with the dry wood and moss we'd brought for the purpose. It worked well and stopped the water from coming through.

Julian and I sat on either side of the raft, digging our long paddles deep into the ocean. We had to row at exactly the same time or we would send the raft spinning. It took us a few minutes but we soon got the hang of it. We followed the coastline for an hour or two, all the while keeping up each other's spirits by singing silly songs and telling riddles. (Julian rarely lets himself be silly like this and I must say it was awfully good fun to see!) After a while, I stopped seeing sea birds so I knew the current was coming up soon. We had to row across it quickly or risk the current dragging us miles out to sea. Crossing the current was like paddling across a swift river, only this river was as strong as the ocean!

When we entered the current, the ocean spray hit us hard. We were constantly wet and cold.

The waves in the current were quite turbulent. Each rise and fall of a wave tipped the raft at an extreme angle. Waves crashed on to us. At first the waves were just a few feet high. Then they rapidly grew into walls of water nearly as tall as Julian. We secured ourselves to the raft with ropes so we wouldn't wash overboard.

"Julian, when the next wave starts to rise, paddle as deep and fast as you can," I shouted. "We've got to make it over the wave crest or we'll capsize."

The wave started to rise and grow. We pulled our paddles hard through the waves. Our arms were burning with the strain of moving the awkward hulking raft up the wall of water looming before us. At last, the raft began to ride up the wave.

"Julian, keep it up, old boy! We're almost there!"

Using the last bit of strength left in our arms we crested the wave and rode smoothly down the other side. We had made it across the current!

"Well done!" called Julian.

I smiled back at him. "We just need to paddle about a mile into shore," I said.

We were both soaked and utterly worn out, but my goodness me! What an exciting adventure that was! I shall be looking to do some white water rafting as soon as ever I can!

Hoorah! We made it!

Chapter Nine

The Culprit Captured

George and Julian beached the raft just outside St Agnes harbour and immediately dashed to the authorities. Julian took the lead and wisely told the police nothing about the Five's hunt for the Royal Dragon. He calmly and clearly told a bemused officer that two children and a dog were stranded out on Riddle Island and that a police boat must be sent for them at once.

The plodding officer clearly didn't believe a word of it so Julian coldly said: "My brother and sister are waiting to be rescued, I tell you. They have no food and very little water. Now, do you want to risk their survival and your job? Or would you rather risk sending a boat out for a couple of hours?"

George chuckled at the officer's obvious discomfort and then watched him hastily call for a boat to be sent out straightaway.

"You two stay here," ordered the officer nervously. "The Sergeant'll want words with you."

"We need to use a phone," said Julian in his most grown-up voice, and was shown to a phone in the corner.

George followed him, her head hung low. The time had come for her to call her father. He was at Miss Richards's guest house and just as furious as she'd expected him to be.

"Georgina!" shouted Uncle Quentin. "I am highly disappointed with you and very cross. You and your cousins were due back to St Agnes two days ago. Am I to understand that you've been larking about on the beach?"

"No, Father, I swear it!" replied George, trying to calm her angry father. "Our boat was stolen and it took us some time to build a raft and sail back."

"Your boat was stolen?" asked her father incredulously. "Oh, George. That's a rather tall story, don't you think?"

"Father, it's true. Please just meet us at the St Agnes police station. Julian will explain everything."

When Uncle Quentin arrived, Julian told him what had happened slowly and logically. Uncle Quentin knew that the Five were often getting into scrapes like this one. So he came round and accepted that what George had told him was indeed the truth.

Then George and Julian accompanied Uncle Quentin to the harbour where the police boat would return with the others.

When Dick and Anne saw them, they jumped for joy. "Oh, I can't tell you how happy and relieved we were when the officer told us you two were all right. We were both so worried," burst out Anne.

Timmy jumped from the police boat and bounded straight to George. He licked her hands and face, barking madly. He was so excited to see his mistress again that he couldn't be daunted even by the sight of a frowning Uncle Quentin, looking on disapprovingly at such lavish displays of affection between the Five.

"Well done both of you! I say next time I get to raft with George!" exclaimed Dick.

"Heavens!" laughed George. "There'd better not be a next time. I don't want to be trapped on a desert island ever again! Though the sailing was thrilling!"

Despite the officer's threat that the Sergeant would want to speak to the Five that day, Uncle Quentin wouldn't hear of it. In a moment of rare empathy, he saw how worn out we all were and insisted that we be interviewed tomorrow. For tonight, we were to return to the guest house for an enormous hot dinner and warm comfortable beds!

On the morning of 31st August, Uncle Quentin ushered us into the police station. We were shown into the office of Sergeant Grayling, a dignified and imposing man with a firm manner, but someone we came to realise was also fair and honourable.

"My officer tells me that you believe someone stole your boat and camping gear, and deliberately stranded you on Riddle Island," began the Sergeant.

He looked each of us squarely in the eyes. (When we talked about it later, we agreed that his penetrating gaze made us feel he could see right into our hearts!)

"What my officer can't tell me is why you think someone should do such a thing?" Sergeant Grayling let his eyes rest on Julian, sensing that he would speak for all of us.

Julian took a deep breath and began to tell our story – just as we'd agreed it together the night before. Starting with reporter Butlerton's first visit to Kirrin Cottage, and ending with his and George's heroic journey on the raft, Julian reported all the adventures we had experienced in our hunt for the Royal Dragon.

When he had finished, we all held our breath and waited to see what Sergeant Grayling would say next.

"Well young man," he began. "You have explained everything very clearly. But kidnapping and theft with intent to cause harm are very serious accusations." The Sergeant paused for a moment. "I just want to make sure I understand you correctly. You believe this woman, this Beverly Butlerton, has committed these crimes against you because ... ?"

"As I've stated, Sir, she's after the treasure, the Royal Dragon," said Julian calmly, and the rest of us nodded profusely, with Timmy adding his own, barked, affirmative.

"Master Kirrin," continued Sergeant Grayling kindly. "You understand that this story is very hard to believe. Can you prove that there's a treasure?"

"We have this map." Julian held out the hundred-year-old scrap of paper. The Sergeant looked at it briefly and handed it back to Julian. "And we have our great-great-great-grandfather's papers, and those of the Duke of Dibeltoynn, and all the other evidence we've found."

The Sergeant smiled, but not in a patronizing way. He looked rather proud of us, in fact.

"Well, let's not worry about the treasure just yet. Now about this reporter," he continued. "Can you prove she is the one who took your boat?"

Dick showed the tracings he'd made of the two rogue footprints on Riddle Island. He said they were fresh and taken soon after the crime. Sergeant Grayling could see that the footprints couldn't possibly be ours. Then Dick produced the most vital piece of evidence we had – the broken red heel he had found on the beach.

"Sergeant, you can find this culprit right now," said Julian. "I have a sketch of her right here and believe she is still on St Agnes."

The Sergeant stroked his chin, clearly deep in thought. After a moment, he turned to his officers and ordered them to round up Beverly Butlerton and anyone they might find with her. "When you find her, make sure you also find her shoes," he said.

We Five smiled at each other – we knew that Sergeant Grayling believed us!

Uncle Quentin set off to rearrange our railway tickets for that evening, while we Five waited at the police station for any news of Butlerton. George and Timmy were growing restless and irritable when, suddenly, there was a great commotion outside. Three officers had both Butlerton and a man (who we could only imagine was her accomplice) in their grasp, and were trying to bring them into the police station while the reporter screamed at them and the man struggled to break free.

Finally, Butlerton and her accomplice, who we learned was named Lenny Gouche, were handcuffed and ushered in front of Sergeant Grayling.

"Good day, Madam, Sir," said the Sergeant, with a cold glint in his eye.

"Why have you arrested me? What is going on?" shouted the reporter. Lenny Gouche remained silent.

"Are you Miss Beverly Butlerton?" asked the Sergeant.

"Yes, of course I am, you idiot. And I am a journalist of Fleet Street and will see that you pay for treating me so horrendously. Let me go at once!"

Goodness! That woman was certainly formidable in her anger! But Sergeant Grayling didn't appear to be put out by her one bit.

Quite calmly, he said, "Miss Butlerton. You are here about very serious matters. We have reason to believe that you stole a sailing boat and left four defenceless children, and their dog," he glanced at Timmy, "stranded on Riddle Island. They could have been terribly hurt."

Miss Butlerton turned around and noticed us for the first time. Several expressions crossed her face in quick succession: shock, fear, anger and then fury!

"YOU!" she spat through clenched teeth. "You brats have ruined everything!"

"So, you do know these children," said Sergeant Grayling. "Do you admit to leaving them stranded?"

"I did no such thing. Besides you can't prove such ridiculous charges!"

Sergeant Grayling made Butlerton and Gouche step on to Dick's footprint drawings. They were a perfect fit. Just then, another officer came into the office.

Sergeant Grayling looked up at him. "Did you find them?" he asked.

"Yes, sir," replied the officer, and pulled out a pair of red, high-heeled shoes, one with its heel missing. It was, of course, the perfect match for the heel that Dick had discovered on the beach! Even so, Butlerton wasn't prepared to give up that easily.

"That's not proof!" she cried. "Why would I want to leave these horrid children stranded on a desert island?"

Unfortunately for Butlerton, a surprise visitor had entered the police station. It was Harbourmaster Rivers. He looked relieved to see us. "Thank goodness you children are unharmed!"

"Rivers, what do you know about this?" asked Grayling curiously.

"The children's sailing boat, *Island Drifter*, Sir. I found it drifting in the bay yesterday. I thought these kids might be taking the boat out again, and that's why they didn't bring it back to me themselves. But it was still there today and I got worried. These are good, polite children, you see. They wouldn't just abandon the boat like that. I ran right over here to report them missing."

"Did you see anything else?" asked Sergeant Grayling.

"Yes I did. Yesterday, I saw a man and a woman rowing away from the sailboat. Rowing fast, they were, like the devil was after them. I yelled for them to stop but it did no good."

"Are these the two that you saw?"

"Why yes! Yes they are! Those are the very two I saw fleeing from the *Island Drifter*. How extraordinary!"

"You'll testify to that in court will you?" confirmed Sergeant Grayling.

"Absolutely, Sergeant, of course. I'm just relieved the children are unharmed."

"Very well, I've heard enough, lock them away Officer Smallwood."

The officer led Lenny Gouche away, but Butlerton would not be moved.

"NO!" she screamed. "NO! You can't lock me up, I must find the treasure! I'd have found it already if it weren't for these meddling children. My family has sought that treasure for generations. And I was so close to finding it … so close."

We Five were stunned by her admission and thrilled to hear that our theories concerning Butlerton were all correct. We could tell that Sergeant Grayling still wasn't convinced about the story of the treasure but, looking at us, he suggested that Butlerton might want to tell him exactly what she knew about this so-called treasure.

And that's when Beverly Butlerton, Fleet Street reporter, descendent of the notorious jewel thief Nathaniel Lunbertot, and a greedy villain in her own right, finally gave her confession.

Dear Anne, who could take dictation at an alarming speed (even without the help of shorthand) took Butlerton's confession down in her diary, word for word. We have transcribed it here for you, exactly as she told it to Sergeant Grayling that day.

"My great-great-grandfather was a magnificent man. Simply brilliant. A genius, some might say. Certainly, he is a legend in the Butlerton family, which is in fact our real name. Nathaniel Butlerton masterminded some of the most intricate, infamous and perplexing jewel robberies of the 19th Century. He was a master of disguise, able to impersonate anyone from the most common chimneysweep to the most regal king. The Royal Dragon of Siam was his most daring robbery. Not even the crown jewels were as closely guarded as the Dragon. He simply had to have it – it became an obsession to him and he planned its robbery for several years before he finally pulled it off.

"It is widely reported (by people who are knowledgeable about these things) that Nathaniel planned to sell the Dragon. He could certainly have made many millions of pounds for it – every collector in the world wanted that piece. But that isn't true. Nathaniel wasn't a greedy man, or at least not for money. He wanted the Dragon for himself. He wanted to pass it down through our family.

"But then that righteous, do-gooder the Duke stole it from Nathaniel! I don't suppose you regard that as stealing, do you Sergeant? Well, that's what it was. The Duke of Dibeltoynn stole it from my great-great-grandfather and tasked the renowned Captain Kirrin with the job of returning it to Siam. But they failed! Hah! Nathaniel outwitted them. He was a skilled seaman and easily convinced Captain Kirrin to appoint him as a member of the Peregrine's *crew. As his Navigator no less, a very trusted position. And perfect for Nathaniel's plan.*

"Nathaniel had men working for him practically everywhere. Foolish, greedy men who thought they were his accomplices. In fact, they were nothing more than pawns to Nathaniel. Spike Spencer was just such a man. A clumsy wrecker who worked for the Lighthouse Brigade. Between them, they wrecked the Peregrine. *Nathaniel just had time to reclaim the Dragon and meet Spike on a sailing boat nearby. But the waters were crawling with police and officials. They were forced to hide the treasure and planned to come back for it when things had quietened down.*

"Well, Spike was stupid, but not stupid enough to believe that Nathaniel wouldn't try to double-cross him. The fool insisted on a treasure map, which they would tear in half, forcing them to come back for the treasure together. Nathaniel must have been delighted by this suggestion – for it gave him the perfect opportunity to cheat Spike! Nathaniel drew the map indicating where they had buried the treasure. On the same piece of parchment, he wrote the instructions needed to pinpoint the exact spot. He tore the parchment in two, and gave Spike the half that showed the location only – the part that Nathaniel had easily memorized and could never forget. Spike was satisfied.

"But neither was able to return to the Dragon again. They were arrested together, some weeks later. My great-great-grandfather was hung for his crimes. Spike was jailed for some years and then was apparently drowned at sea. I'm certain he never found the Dragon again. He was too stupid to find its hiding place without Nathaniel's directions. Spike's half of the map was never found. Or, at least, not by any Butlerton anyway.

"My family have sought the Dragon ever since. Each generation, every descendent, hoping to be the one to claim Nathaniel's prize. But we lacked the other half of the map!

"You see, Nathaniel never had time to tell his children where the treasure was buried. So I don't know. I have often wondered whether a Kirrin might have found the other half of the map? I wonder that still ... is it possible that these pathetic, annoying little children have outfoxed a Butlerton and solved the mystery of the Royal Dragon? But, of course, that isn't possible, is it? After all, they are only children."

No one had spoken during Butlerton's monologue – too fascinated by the story she wove. We Five had been able to puzzle out some of her story from the clues we had found, but the picture she painted of Nathaniel Butlerton was even more terrifying than we had supposed.

Finally, George could hold her tongue no longer. "Your great-great grandfather was a despicable thief who stole the Royal Dragon from the King of Siam. His treachery set off a terrible civil war that devastated an entire country!"

Butlerton smiled sadly. "Well," she said. "It's lost forever now, I suppose." She hung her head in defeat, visibly losing all hope of recovering Spike Spencer's half of the treasure map, or ever finding the hidden treasure.

Sergeant Grayling brought the situation back to reality. "Officer Smallwood, please record Miss Butlerton's possessions and read her her rights. Miss Butlerton, you are being arrested for stealing and leaving these children stranded. I don't believe that the Police can do anything to solve the 'mystery of the Royal Dragon'. Children, you are free to go."

"Thank goodness," said Uncle Quentin, who had returned almost without our noticing him. "Children, everything is ready. Our tickets are arranged but I must call Miss Richards and have her send our luggage to the railway station. You five wait for me outside."

We made our way outside, all of us except one.

Anne had remained behind to watch Miss Butlerton's arrest. She felt betrayed by the reporter, and foolish for having fallen for her kindness. Above all, Anne felt responsible for leading Butlerton to us, both on the train to Penzance and on Riddle Island. She wanted to see for herself that Butlerton was being arrested and that justice had been done.

As it turned out, Anne left that scene in the police station with rather a lot more than she had expected ...

Anne's Diary - 31st August, 1959

On the train from Penzance to Kirrin

Dear Diary,

Uncle Quentin is sitting with us in the carriage so I can't share my extraordinary news with the others. I simply might burst with the pressure of not being able to tell them! I hope that writing things out here will help me remain calm, or else I'm sure that I shall jump up and blurt it all out for anyone to hear!

The others went outside to wait for Uncle Quentin but I was strangely rooted to the spot – unable to look away from Miss Butlerton as the policeman went through her handbag and recorded its contents. I can't explain why, I simply felt that I shouldn't go but keep watching.

She had all the usual things one might expect to find in a lady's handbag. A make-up compact, lipstick, a hairbrush and purse. She had a small pile of her business cards, a notebook and tape recorder, several pens, a nail file and a torch. Just when I thought her bag was empty, the officer pulled out something that made me gasp. It was an old, folded piece of parchment!

The officer didn't know what to make of it. "What's this?" he asked, unfolding it.

"It's nothing," said Miss Butlerton in a strange voice.

"What is this gibberish?" asked the officer again. "What does it mean?"

"As you say, Officer, it's just gibberish," said Miss Butlerton. "Just a silly rhyme I've been working on that I thought might amuse my readers. It's rubbish, that's all."

"This is rather funny paper to be scribbling on, Miss." The officer was clearly suspicious of it. "Still, if you say it's just rubbish, Miss, then I don't suppose you'll mind if I throw it in the bin, will you?"

The officer looked at Miss Butlerton, challenging her to contradict him. I think he knew that the parchment was something important and thought he might scare her into confessing what it really was. But she did nothing of the sort.

Oh, Diary! You simply won't believe what I've done!

When the officer led Miss Butlerton away, I went back into that room and took that piece of parchment from the bin! I have it here in the pocket of my dress and I feel that it's burning a hole right through the fabric!

What will the others say when I tell them?!

As the train took us back to Kirrin Cottage and Uncle Quentin sat reading his paper, we Five remained silent and subdued. Our summer holidays were over. We would return to school tomorrow. We had had one of the most thrilling adventures of our days, but we were deflated. Our mystery had remained unsolved. The Royal Dragon remained hidden.

It wasn't until Uncle left to order some food for us that Anne was able to tell us her staggering news. As soon as Uncle was out of sight, Anne pulled out the scrap of parchment she rescued from the police station's rubbish bin.

"I say, what's that, old girl?" asked Dick surprised.

"It can't be!" whispered George.

"Is it?" asked Julian.

Anne nodded, a beaming smile shining from her face. "It is," she said. "Butlerton was forced to give it up in the police station. The officer didn't know what it was and threw it in the bin. I'm afraid I stole it!" she finished. Anne looked terrified and proud all at the same time.

"Well," chuckled Dick. "It was already thrown away, so it's not really stealing, Annie."

Julian laughed too. "I'm not so sure of that," he said. "But I am awfully glad you fished it out of the bin."

"Genius! That's what it is!" cried George, finding her voice again. "Oh, Anne! You brilliant old thing. You've done it! You've solved the mystery!"

"Well, actually, I haven't," said Anne. "You see, it doesn't really make any sense … "

THE HAND OF THE DRAGON
DOTH MAKE A KING
HE SLEEPS IN STONE
A GLITTERING THING
CAPTURED IN THE LIGHT
OF A BRAND NEW DAY
ITS PLACE IS RIGHT WHERE
THE LAST BRICK'S LAID

The Treasure Room

Walls: 100 bricks in every wall.
Width: 10 ft by 10 ft square.
Height: 6 ft tall.

Famous Five Mission Message

Sadly, Anne was right. We read the other half of the map, but couldn't understand how it would lead to the Royal Dragon of Siam. We pondered the words on that piece of parchment over and over again. We never were able to return to Riddle Island and, eventually, we forgot about the unsolved mystery as other mysteries demanded our attention instead.

Now we are grown, and you are the child adventurers, not us. The Mystery of the Royal Dragon has perplexed us Kirrins for more than 100 years. All that time, the Royal Dragon of Siam has remained hidden in the Treasure Room, beneath the Martello tower on Riddle Island. We think it's time to solve the mystery once and for all. Don't you?

All the clues you need to solve the mystery are in this Book. The map that was torn in two is in one piece again – we enclose it here for you. Julian has also drawn an architectural plan of the Treasure Room, detailing every brick in every wall, with exact measurements clearly labelled.

George says that 'the villain Lunbertot' must have had a fine sense of humour, for, you see, he invented a riddle to conceal the Dragon on Riddle Island. Can you solve the riddle that Nathaniel Butlerton set? Can you work out the location of the Royal Dragon?

We do believe you can.

Go to www.famousfive.co.uk to check your answer. We do so hope that you will be right.

Good luck!

Julian Dick Anne George

The Famous Five
In memory of Timmy

Further Information

We hope that you've learned many things as you've helped us on our hunt for the Royal Dragon of Siam, but remember that this is just the beginning. If you want to be the best possible adventurer you must now continue your training and seek expert help from professional adventurers. Here are some organizations that can help you continue the good work you've started.

- MENSA -

www.mensa.org
www.us.mensa.org

- Places of Interest -

www.nationaltrust.org.uk
www.english-heritage.org.uk
www.nationaltrust.org.au
www.nsw.nationaltrust.org.au
www.nationaltrust.org

- Rambling/Hiking -

www.ramblingclubs.com
www.americanhiking.org

- Camping/Adventure Holidays -

www.youthinformation.com
www.oeg.net.au
www.outwardbound.net

- Nature Conservation -

www.greenpeace.org
www.nature.org
www.acfonline.org.au

- Country Code -

www.countrysideaccess.gov.uk/things_to_know
www.imba.com/about/trail_rules.html

- First Aid -

www.cdc.gov/nasd/menu/topic/firstaid.html
www.stjohn.org.au
www.redcross.org.uk

- Sailing -

www.ussailing.org
www.rya.org.uk
www.sailing.org

- Climbing -

www.thebmc.co.uk
www.americanalpineclub.com
www.sportclimbingaustralia.org.au/1.0/home
www.theuiaa.org

- Fishing -

www.gofishing.co.uk
www.ifishonline.com
www.fishingaustralia.com.au

- Meteorology -

www.bom.gov.au/lam
www.srh.noaa.gov/srh/jetstream
www.bbc.co.uk/weather/weatherwise/
www.metoffice.gov.uk

- Tall Ships -

www.tallships.org
www.sailtraining.org
www.tallshipsaustralia.com

- Maritime History -

www.nmm.ac.uk
www.nps.gov/history/maritime
www.aamh.asn.au

Index

Picture Credits

13-Brown Paper--Valery Potapova
18-19-Shipwreck--Dhoxax
18-19-Lifejacket--Maxstockphoto
18-19-Life belt--Romanchuck Dimitry
20-Old Book--Nik
20-Old Book--igor kisselev
20-Old Book--Najin
21-Background--Fotoar
25-House--Peter Elvidge
27-Background--Grzegorz Slemp
27-Stamp--Albert Campbell
28-Ships Plan & Castle--Chen Ping Hung
30-Captain's Log--Stoupa
30-Peregrine-- Sergey Prygov
31-Background--Tatiana53
31-Coat of Arms--Ann Triling
31-Lions--Black Ink Designers, Corp.
31-Wax Seal--Wiedzma
34-35-Ruler--Photo Create
36-37-Padlock and Code--Jenny Horne
41-Timetable Background--Vladimir Caplinskij
41-Ticket Background--Franssonkane
41-Pocket Watch--Jaroslaw Brzychcy
41-Train--Betacam-SP
42-43-First aid kit--Jyothi Joshi
42-43-Torch--Marc Dietrich
42-43-Tent in bag--Luminis
42-43-Camp stove--Marek Chech
42-43-Swiss army knife--8781118005
42-43-Black and orange backpack--Igor XIII
42-43-Blue backpack--J Helgason
42-43-Pile of packs--MaxStockPhoto
42-43-Red backpack--Natalia Silverina
44-First aid kit--Borzee
44-Wipes--Maciej Walczak
44-Aspirin--Nix
44-Bandage--Brian Tan
44-Tweezers--Mitar
44-Gloves--Michelle Cox
44-Ointment--J. J. Lim
44-Plasters--Cloki
44-Scissors--Spe
44-Safety pins--Gavin Anderson
44-Bacon--Niderlander
45-Pasta--Pixelman
45-Bagel--IIllia Shalamaev
45-Crackers--Travis Manley
45-Tuna Tin--TIina Rencelj
45-Nuts--Katrina Leigh
45-Jell Beans--Feng Yu
48-49-Bed--Steve Lovegrove
48-49-Nametag--J Helgason
48-49-Doorway--Stephen Coburn
48-49-Keys--Tiplyashin Anatoly
48-49-Sugar Cubes--Olga Shelego
48-49-Chicken--RGBSpace
48-49-Kitchen--Sklep Spozywczy
48-49-Woman--Stephen Leech
48-49-Cows--Eric Iselee
48-49-Monkey--Peter Doomen
50-51-Motorbike--Konstantin Tavrov
50-51-Clock--Mike Flippo
50-51-Woman--Darren Baker
50-51-Roller Coaster--Cary Kalscheuer
50-51-Skier--Ilja Masik
50-51-House--Andrey Armyagov
50-51-Penguin--Jan Martin Will
50-51-Boy--Larisa Loftiskaya
50-51-Compass--Nikolay Okhitin
50-51-Fruit--Denis Pepin
52-Suitcase--Robyn Mackenzie
61-Train--HFNG
65-Compass--Tischenko Irina
67-Slice of Bread--Tomek_
67-Honey Jar--Morgan Lane Photography
74-75-Tunnel--Peter Doomen
74-75-Fireplace--Rachel L Sellers
74-75-Library--Photgl
74-75-Stately Home--David Holmes
74-75-Panelling--Rohit Seth
79-Postcard Front--rgbspace
79-Postcard Back--Stephen Aaron Rees
81-Hamper--Stephen Coburn
82-83-Compass--Geoff Deiderfield
82-83-Compass+Map--Galyna Andrushko
82-83-Compass--Zygimantas Cepaitis
82-83-Map--Jeff Dalton
85-Penknife--Design56
88-Tent in Woods--Donald Joski
88-Wooded Valley--Fauxware
89-Woodland Stream--Szabo Photography
89-Wasp--Oliver Johannes Uhrig
92-93-Tent--Chris Hill
92-93-Camp Fire--Stanislav Komogorov
92-93-Two Tents--Davis S Baker
92-93-Campsite--Vera Bogaerts
98-99-Desert--Curtis Kautzer
100-102-Marshmallow--Johann Helgason
104-105-Chilli--Joe Gough
104-105-Ribs--George P Choma
104-105-Campfire--Galyna Andrushko
104-105-Chicken & Veg --
Martin Ezequiel Gardeazabal
106-109-Rowanberries--Kmitu
106-109-Purslane--Nathalie Dulex
106-109-Sorrel--Fotosav
106-109-Bilberries--Nialat
106-109-Nettles--Peter Guess
106-109-Watercress--Ewa Brozek
106-109-Chanterelle--Laura Frenkel
106-109-Wild Chervil--Knud Neilsen
106-109-Elderberries--Anette Linnea Rasmussen
106-109-Samphire--Steve McWilliam
106-109-Ceps--Dainis Derics
106-109-Wild Ramsons--Aleksander Bolbot
106-109-Morels--Klaus Rainier Krieger
106-109-Blackberries--Liga Lauzuma
106-109-Dandelion--Agita
106-109-Chestnuts--Paul Maguire
106-109-Elderflower--Gyorgy Eger
106-109-Apples--Sergei Didyk
106-109-Pine Needels--Odze
111-Cloth--Najin
111-Knot--Milushkina Anastasiya
114-Rabbit--Joel Blit
114-Red Deer--Richard Bowden
115-Bat--Angela Farley
115-Badger--Markabond
115-Barn Owl--Nick Biemans
116-Fox--Ronnie Howard
116-Adder--Tomo Jesenicnik
116-Hedgehog--Chris Turner
117-Sparrowhawk--Tomo Jesenicnik
117-Squirrel--Sharon D
118-Woodland--Dhoxax
119-Stile & Gate--verityjohnson
119-Dog Walking--1846281426
120-Woodland River--Evgeni Gitlits
120-Rubbish--maxstockphoto
121-Country Lake--David Hughes
124-Mountains--Mary Terriberry
124-125-Woodland Path--Stanislav Bokach
124-125-Whistle--Pjorg
124-125-Swiss Army Knife--Jonas Staub
124-125-Bandage--Ronald Sumners
124-125-Pack--Natalia Silverina
124-125-Matches--Vladislav Sabanov
124-125-Pill Bottle--NIX
124-125-Lotion Bottle--Temovoy Dmitry
126-127-Forest--Suzanne Tucker
126-127-Girl Whistling--Poprugin Aleksey
126-127-Panic--Adrian Moisei
126-127-Horizon--Niserin
126-127-Footprints--Jakez
128-129-Animal Print--William Attard McCarthy
128-129-Muddy Print--Pichugin Dmitry
128-129-Barb Wire--Anita Charlton
128-129-Sand Print-
Hirlesteanu Constantin- Ciprian
131-Woodland River--Coko
132-133-River--Geir Olav Lyngfjell
132-133-River--Nataliya Peregudova
136-Rope--Kmitu
136-Quicksand Sign--Kerry L. Werry
136-Panic--Adrian Moisei
140-143-CPR 1--PRISM_68
140-143-CPR 2--PRISM_68
140-143-CPR 3--PRISM_68
140-143-Scrape--Katrina Brown
140-143-Hypothermia--Tomasz TrojanowskiI
140-143-Med Pack--ASP
140-143-Bandage 1--EDW
140-143-Bandage 2--EDW
150-Envelope Back--Peter Zaharov
151-Old Paper--vnlit
151-Marble--ANP
156-Old Files--vnlit
157-Background--pdtnc
158-Dragon--Sandra Caldwell
158-Background--akva
159-Magnifying Glass--Orla
164-166-Pinnochio--Faberfoto
164-166-Crossed Fingers--Jorge Salcedo
164-166-Voice Clues--Robert Studio
166-167-Reason to Confess --Steven Pepple
166-167-Interrogate--Marcin Balcerzak
172-173-RNLI--Mark William Penny
172-173-Sailing Boat--Eric Gevaert
172-173-Radio--Anton Gvozdikov
172-173-Torch--Jaroslaw Grudzinski
172-173-Compass--Lebanmax
172-173-Whistle--Andresr
172-173-Bucket--Morgan Lane Photography
172-173-Oars--Jennifer Stone
172-173-Flare Gun--Leo
172-173-Food Supplies--Scott Rothtein
174-175-Yacht --Gary Blakeley
174-175-Yacht--Salvador Garcia Gil
174-175-Sailing--Photosky4TCom
182-183-Climbing Wall--Mypokcik
182-183-Rock Climber--Galyna Andrushko
182-183-Climbing Helmets--
Oleg Kozlov, Sophy Kozlova
182-183-Climbing Shoes--Tom Grundy
190-Torch--Claire VD
193-Background--Topal
195-Shells--Robert D Pinna
198-Police Line--Loren Rodgers
199-Evidence Tag--Stephen Sweet
199-Fingerprints-Bruce Rolff
204-205-River--J. Helgason
210-Cirrus--Thierry Maffeis
210-Cirrocumulus--Jostein Hauge
210-Altocumulus--Peter Blottman
211-Stratus--salamanderman
211-Nimbostratus--Irene Teesalu
211-Cumulus--Melody Mulligan
211-Cumulonimbus--Carly Rose Hennigan
212-213-Lightning--Daniel E Cutlip
212-213-Lightning 2--Salamanderman
212-213-Lightning 3--Naumov Roman
212-213-Fallen tree--Jessica Bethke
216-217-Message in Bottle--Olaf Schlueter
216-217-Blowing Whistle--Photobar
216-217-Signal Fire--
Shironina Lidiya Alexandrovna
216-217-SOS--1846281426
218-Rope--Izaokas Sapiro
220-221-Rafting--A. S. Zain
223-Watch-Bruce Shippee
223-224-Horizon and Sun--Niserin
229-Mackerel--StudioNewmarket
Various-Background George's Diary--
Natalia Siverina
Various-Background Dick's Diary--
George Pappas
Various-Background Julians Diary--Stocksnapp
Various-Background Anne's Diary--
Whitney Krueger
Various-Background--Tatiana53